Stories of St]

Stories, articles, pictures & poems
by the people of St Leonards

edited by Kay Green

Earlyworks Press

Stories of St Leonards

stories, articles, pictures & poems
by the people of St Leonards

Copyright Information

Printed in the UK
by MPG Books Group

ISBN 978-1-906451-66-0

Published by Earlyworks Press
Creative Media Centre,
45 Robertson St, Hastings,
Sussex TN34 1HL

www.earlyworkspress.co.uk

Dedication

To all the people of St Leonards,
past and present, who have made it such a
fascinating place to be.

Editor's Introduction

I am going to confess right at the start that I lived in St Leonards for at least five years before I knew I did. Along the seafront, the distinction between Hastings and St Leonards is quite clear. There are two town centres, each with a character of its own. Inland, it's a different story. I wrote "Hastings" whenever I wrote my address but, in pavement-social terms, I lived in "Silverhill". Everyone knows Silverhill is in St Leonards now, because when the new ASDA opened there, the local residents gave them a round telling off for announcing it as their "new Hastings store". Apologies and corrections abounded, and the new store now has "St Leonards" on its sign.

I'd forgotten all about this strength of feeling until we launched *Visions of Hastings* and several people came up to me at the launch and said, 'what about St Leonards then?' so I started asking people what was special about St Leonards and received an amazing variety of answers. So here it is, the sister-book for *Visions of Hastings*, fizzing with extraordinary stories of St Leonards – and I know we've hardly scratched the surface. I caught the tail-ends of so many aspects of the community history while we were preparing the book – I dug my heels in when I did purely because one must draw the line somewhere. But you will see, when you get to the last article in this book, it's not easy to know where to draw it!

The characters and fortunes of the town (or towns) of Hastings and St Leonards have changed a lot over the years. Once upon a time, they were naturally divided by the great chunk of chalk known as the White Rock which, until its removal in 1834, stood on the foreshore and precluded any thought of an easy road between the two. Commemorated now in the names of the hotel, the theatre and other institutions on the border between the boroughs, its remains leave plenty of scope for communication between east and west.

St Leonards has had the good fortune (some would say) to have been the site of projects by several architects and designers. Its Victorian heyday is typified by the creations of James Burton.

Working in the era of utilitarianism, as well as creating many of the still grand (if somewhat delicate) frontages, Burton was responsible for the name "Mercatoria", for the part of St Leonards where he intended the merchants to live. We can only thank our lucky stars he never got around to the launderers' quarter, which was to be known as "Lavatoria". Here's the family grave, atop the hill at West Ascent...

No, not *that* West Hill, *St Leonards* West Hill. Thanks to this whole one-town-two-towns business, Hastings is probably the only town in the world that sits in a valley with a West Hill on *both* sides.

As well as Burton's creations, many impressive town houses were built in St Leonards. The social divide between their occupants and the Hastings community typified by the fishing families of the old town, was immense – and it has never been forgotten by the Old Hastings families. If you want evidence, go search out an Old Town band known as "Rude Knot To" and listen to their ballad, "Hastings Nights", a lesser known Romeo and Juliet of a tale.

Burton's work began to crumble as the Victorian era passed away but there were more architects waiting to make their mark on

St Leonards, most famously the "Concrete King", Sidney Little, who named his most famous work "Bottle Alley" (rivalling "Lavatoria" in its invitation to sniggerers) but there is one more item of grand design that deserves a mention of its own. Possibly the largest *tromp d'oeil* on the south coast.

Try walking an unwary visitor along the seafront from Hastings to St Leonards. Tell them you're heading for "The Marina" and they'll probably say they didn't know St Leonards had a marina. Nod wisely, hold your peace and, as you pass along Hastings seafront, watch your visitor exclaim and point out that they can indeed see a huge cruise ship coming in to dock.

They have of course spotted St Leonards' art-deco triumph, Marine Court.

I tell this story here because, when people started telling me I couldn't leave it at *Visions of Hastings*, their first argument was that we had scurrilously included Joe Fearn's poem about Marine Court "sailing down the road to Hastings".

"*To* Hastings," they said, "*toooo,* not *iiiiin.* It's not *in* Hastings, it's in *St Leonards!*"

Marine Court is no longer a new building and, in many people's eyes, it's too soon for the Victorian wonders to be attractively old so for most of my adult life, Hastings was the smart bit and St Leonards was – well, you know, a bit past its best. But the fortunes of towns change under your feet. During the last few decades, the currents of life have brought an extraordinary variety of new people to St Leonards. They have brought with them art galleries, festivals, and an enormous range of community projects and enterprises. There are those who call Brighton "London by the sea" but I met a resident of St Leonards a while back who said she felt she was living in "Portobello by the sea".

In the pages that follow, you will find a small selection of the many stories that have unfolded in St Leonards. My heartfelt thanks to all those who offered up photos, artworks, poems, stories and articles: to Steve Amos, winner of the "Stories of St Leonards" competition and all those who were shortlisted and have joined in the compiling of the book, to Tony Frost, whose range of photo-journalism, poetry and collaborations with various local characters is without equal, Alex Ntung who is himself a marvellous example of how the wide world has come to St Leonards and added to the magic, and Victoria Seymour, a veritable fount of information and encouragement to any local history project.

This book is to be launched at Books Born in Hastings 2012... and as we named this, our annual celebration of local books and writing before all this happened, I'm already preparing for everyone to come up and tell me that the posters for the event should say Books Born in Hastings *and St Leonards!*

Kay Green March 2012

Contents

Secret Corners

There are 13 "secret corners" pages in this book. If you know where any of them are – or if you go out and find them after you've read about them, please take your copy of this book along. If you send us a photo of you and the book in one of the secret corners, along with a letter or article about what that place means to you, we'll put them on the website. Please email your photos to services@earlyworkspress.co.uk or deliver them to The Creative Media Centre, 45 Robertson Street Hastings, TN34 1HL.

Bike Ride to the Bathing Pool

by Steve Amos

My sons and I watch them emerge from a sea mist – magical, illuminated bicycles, with fairy lights around their frames and wheels. Many of the riders wear the clothes of a bygone age – men in bow ties and waistcoats, young women in white lace dresses, looking like they're heading for an Edwardian tea party. But these exotic cyclists are participants in the 'From Pier to Eternity' bike ride, part of the 2011 Coastal Currents Arts Festival. Tonight's destination is the old St Leonards bathing pool, once the site of a great amphitheatre that was the crowning triumph of Sidney Little, Hastings and St Leonards' 'concrete king'.

Borough Engineer Little was commissioned to construct the pool in 1931. The statistics are impressive – at 330 feet by 90 feet it was big enough to host Olympic events. Ten metre high diving boards rose into the air, and there was seating for 2500 spectators. It opened to great excitement in June 1933, and made a profit in its first year. Unfortunately it was never to do so again.

The scale of Little's ambition was disproportionate to the pool's location. Not to put too fine a point on it, St Leonards was never likely to find itself hosting Olympic swimming and diving events. Furthermore, the reinforced concrete used in the pool's construction

1

was prone to leaking and costly to repair. By 1946, the council was desperate to get rid of it.

Eventually the site was sold and redeveloped as a holiday camp. The pool was partially filled in, but it remained substantial and formed the centrepiece. An advertisement for the camp in the mid-1960s claimed it provided 'The *finest* swimming facilities ever – one million gallons of sparkling sea water which is continuously purified and sterilised'.

By the 1970s the availability of cheap package holidays in warmer climes meant that traditional British holidays were no longer in demand. The camp closed and was then demolished, and in 1986 the leaky old pool was grassed over.

Back to 2011, and the wave of brightly lit bicycles sweeps on to the site. A projector is set up and soon black and white footage of the pool in the 1950s appears on a crumbling wall. Young men swoop like Tom Daley from the 10 metre high diving boards, while pretty girls in swimming costumes smile and pose for the camera. I watch these monochrome ghosts then look out across the barren site as the misty darkness descends. My kids lark about on the grass, but soon all I can see of them are the LED badges they made at a Coastal Currents workshop, flashing red, blue and green in the night.

A couple watch the film footage and reminisce sadly about what has been lost. Once we had 'the *finest* swimming facilities ever' – a bathing pool big enough to host the Olympics, where young men dived, pretty girls posed and the sun always shone – albeit in black and white. But along with the losses there are gains, like this crazy

2

coloured bike ride 'from pier to eternity'. In the end we're all heading for the same place, so we might as well enjoy the ride.

Pictures with this text by kind permission of Radiator Arts

The Bathing Pool Site

Identifying the Body, 1066

It was all over. Whether or not he died with an arrow in his eye is still open to debate. That it happened in Hastings is definitely not open to debate. The Battle of Hastings happened in Battle. That's why it's called Battle. So when people tell you King Harold died in Battle, don't ask where. You shouldn't ask when either. It's the one historical date we all definitely know.

Does anyone bother though, to remember the plight of Edith, Harold's wife, searching the grizzly remains on the Senlac – the Field of Blood – to discover his fate? Someone remembered. And they remembered a rather more romantic version of the search than I did.

The trouble is, as memorials go this one isn't working too well. Just as the Angel of the North became 'The Tart with the Ironing Board', so this tribute to Edith's moment of tragedy has become known locally as 'that statue of the woman strangling her husband'.

KG

6

Bo-Peep Body

by Jonathan Broughton

Early on the morning of 25th August 1891, Edgar Dunk, a platelayer[*], walked through Bo Peep tunnel on his way to work. In the gloom, he thought he saw a bundle of rags lying beside the track, but on closer inspection discovered the body of a woman. There was blood under her neck and her face was black with dirt.

---

[*] A **platelayer** or trackman is a railway employee whose job is to inspect and maintain the permanent way of a railway installation.

7

He ran to Warrior Square Station and found Alfred Tichener, a night watchman and porter. Together, they carried the dead woman out of the tunnel. They didn't know who she was, and guessed that she might be in her early to mid-twenties. Only after the doctor had washed the dirt off her face did Alfred recognize her; Agnes Mary Sheather. Aged thirteen. His wife used to give her piano lessons.

Agnes lived with her father, Thomas John, her brothers and stepmother at 9 Alexandra Terrace. She was in service at Mr Cotton's at 79 Warrior Square. Her father had seen her on Monday evening, the 24th August, in the Kings Road, at which time she seemed cheerful, and called out that she would see him tomorrow. Perhaps she was putting on a brave face – her father knew she was unhappy working at Mr Cotton's, but didn't know then that she had just lost her job. She had only been there a week.

Mr Cotton kept a lodging house in Warrior Square and called on Mrs Sheather, Agnes's stepmother, regularly, to collect his coal. On Monday he went round as usual, but on his arrival, Mrs Sheather showed him a letter from Agnes in which she accused him of ill-treating her. "I could not satisfy Mr Cotton in any way." and of neglecting his little boy who, she said, was "half starved."

She also wrote that when Mr Cotton came home drunk, his wife would give him a "good legging."

Mrs Sheather tried to make light of it, saying that Agnes was always making up stories, but Mr Cotton was furious and later confronted Agnes with the letter. He demanded an explanation concerning such slanderous allegations. She denied knowing anything about it, and accused her stepmother of being a "wicked, base woman," and just like her to say such things. She spent all her money on drink, Agnes added.

Mr Cotton, fearing a scandal, told Agnes that he would have to let her go. She could serve out her notice until Saturday. Agnes had her supper, cleared the dining room table and wished Mr and Mrs Cotton good night before going up to her room.

Just before ten thirty, Mr Cotton went out into the hall and found the front door open. Fearing that intruders had broken in, he searched the house, and on entering Agnes's bedroom, found it empty. He assumed that she had decided not to serve out her notice and had returned home. The Sheathers only lived about 200 yards away, on the other side of Warrior Square Station. He needed a drink and went out, calling first at the *Railway Tavern*, and then at the *Yorkshire Grey*. He was home again by eleven.

Agnes would often spend time at Warrior Square Station. It was one of her favourite haunts, and her friend, Kate Russell, who was a laundress, sat with her sometimes.

"What were you doing there?" asked the Chief Constable at the inquest.

"We used to sit and pass remarks on people," replied Kate, laughing.

"Did Agnes ever tell you she was acquainted with any of the porters at the station?" asked the Coroner.

"No sir, she never used to mention anybody."

Agnes often talked to Kate about her future. She said she wanted to be a laundry girl like Kate, because she didn't like service work. If she had to be in service she "would make away with herself," Kate told the inquest. She was very unhappy at home too; her stepmother drank, and her father was a bully.

On that Monday evening, 24th August, William Bird was on duty in the signal box at the station. At some time during the evening, though he couldn't say when, as he was busy, but he thought at around half past ten, a female came up to the box and looked through the window. He didn't think anything of it as this sort of thing often happened. People sometimes mistook the signal box for the parcels room, but as the female turned away he heard her say: "That isn't him."

By 10.30, the gas lamps in the station were turned low, and after the Brighton mail had gone through at ten minutes past twelve, they were turned off. The next train would be a light engine at a quarter to six in the morning. The area around the entrance to the tunnel was almost as dark as the tunnel itself.

William Bird finished work and clocked off at ten to one, leaving Alfred Tichener alone, on duty throughout the night.

Alfred Tichener lived at 15 Southwater Road, and had known Agnes since she was a baby. She called out whenever she spotted him as she crossed the bridge between the two platforms, though at the inquest the station staff denied seeing Alfred ever talk to Agnes, nor had they ever heard her ask for him.

Edgar Dunk, who found her body, told the inquest that Alfred had asked him if the woman was dead. If she was, he said, he would take a board to fetch her out; otherwise he would use a stretcher.

Agnes died from a blow to the "thick part of the temporal bone containing the internal ear." The fracture allowed blood to pour over her brain. Death would have been almost instant.

Mr Henry Colborne, a surgeon who practiced in St Leonards and was the first medical man to examine Agnes's body, agreed with the Coroner that a passing train might have caused the injury, but so too could a wrench hammer, or the point of a crow bar. In fact, if he had seen the body at the mortuary and not at the station, and knew nothing of the circumstances of the girl's death, he would have concluded that she had died from a massive blow to the head caused by a heavy object; not a glancing blow from a passing train.

There were no signs to suggest that she had been "outraged," but neither could it be definitely proved that she was a virgin. She had died, concluded the surgeon, between two and three o'clock, on the morning of 25th August.

At twelve minutes past nine on 9th September 1891, the jury at Hastings Town Hall retired to consider their verdict. The Coroner "regretted that the evidence before them did not, in his mind, enable them to come to a sound conclusion as to how the deceased met her death."

They had clear facts before them. Her death was caused by a fracture to the skull. She had been dismissed from her work at Mr Cotton's lodging house. She had known Alfred Tichener since she was a baby. She had threatened to commit suicide.

These were the facts, but what had they learnt about Agnes? Did the jury speculate about the character of this adolescent girl? She was bored with her life and looked for ways to spice up her dreary existence. She chose to fantasize about the people she knew, and made up stories, wicked stories, untrue stories, but stories that made people take notice of her when she told them.

Or was it just one person whose attention she was after? Did she have a crush on Alfred? Was there perhaps, some deeper feeling between the two of them? Maybe he became alarmed by the intensity of their relationship, and panicked. Or was he fed up with the unwanted attentions of an adolescent girl and, when the opportunity presented itself, lost control and snapped?

10

Her death might have been a terrible accident. When she left Mr Cotton's, did she hide down the Bo Peep tunnel to make people think that she had run away? Give them a good scare. Make them take notice, and then, like a miracle, reappear the next day. Everyone would be so pleased to see that she was safe and sound. But the terrible noise from the passing trains and the suffocating smoke in a confined space may have overwhelmed her.

The jury took twenty minutes to reach their verdict.

"The deceased was found dead in a tunnel; the cause of death was fracture of the skull, but no evidence to show how the fracture was caused."

An open verdict.

So the mystery remains, and now at this distance in time we shall never know how or why Agnes Mary Sheather died. There are only two facts of which we can be certain; the Bo Peep tunnel hid her body. It also hid her death.

Secret Corners of St Leonards No 1

How well do you know St Leonards?

How many of our "secret corners" photos could you
point to on a map? Here's a clue to No 1 – the picture
shows St Leonards Writers at the door of their hideout
– *but where is it?*

The Wreck of the Amsterdam

by Angela Perkins

I suppose most people thought it was about money or position. Of course there was always a certain satisfaction about knowing my name was being passed around the town, although usually it was a whisper, or a quiet word in a corner, or in a scribbled note which was quickly read and tossed into the fire. And so in time they all came to know; if you want something, ask Tom. Brandy? Tom will get it for you. Silk? I'll get a message to my cousin, who'll speak to his friend, who'll tell his brother, who'll get a message to Tom. Tom will find it, or acquire it or somehow get it to you; ask no questions, tell no lies and before you even know for sure that the message has reached its target, it will be done. But ask too many questions, ask how and when and where and suddenly Tom will disappear like a black cat into the darkness and no-one will ever admit that they've ever even heard the name.

I'll admit the rewards were nice – a little sweetener to ease the passage of whatever was your fancy from one hand to another – but it was never just about that. Well, maybe that was the initial temptation, but after that it was so much more. After that it was for the thrill: the danger, walking the narrow line between success and discovery, knowing when to creep and hide, and when the best way to pass unnoticed was to walk tall and confident. And that confidence served me well; a charming word and a few coins were often all it took to persuade the Excise men to look the other way while the Tubmen carried the tubs of brandy or wraps of tobacco deep into the night. And then with the deed done and spirits high, it would be back to *The Bull Inn* for a celebration drink, although we were always clever enough that never a word passed between us as to what had just taken place, for fear of who might be listening.

And putting modesty aside, we were good at what we did. I'm proud to say we relied on stealth and our wits rather than knives and guns, though we would have fought like a pack of dogs if the need had ever arisen. For all that we operated outside the law, and many people far greater than I have debated the rights and wrongs of that law, we were bound together by a sense of loyalty and camaraderie as close as any soldier or Customs Officer had for his fellow men. I'll grant that some nights were hard: legs cold and wet from the spray, arms aching from carrying the load, hearts beating from exertion and fear, so hard that they seemed almost to drown out the muffled steady thump of heavy boots on the coast path. But the feeling afterwards, when we were all home and safe in our beds, made it all worthwhile. Even when we were just a whisker away from discovery, when we declared that that was definitely the last time, that feeling would always bring us back, for there's no feeling in the world quite as intoxicating as knowing you're flirting with the hangman's noose. And it would have been the hangman's noose for me because although I pulled my weight as hard as any man there, the planning was mine. It was me they looked to for guidance, for orders. Although I hope I never abused my position, knowing we were a good team and that I needed them as much as they needed me.

But just occasionally we got a job so easy that you'd think a guardian angel was watching over us. And the best of these was unplanned – a gift that landed in our lap unexpectedly, like a posy from a secret admirer. I may be old now, my memory not as sharp as it used to be, but I will never till the day I go to my grave forget the day the *Amsterdam* fetched up on the shore not a stone's throw from *The Bull* in the first month of 1749. Of course, I didn't hear the full story until afterwards but rumour reached us in the preceding week that a Dutch cargo ship was in trouble down the coast and we secretly hoped that the bad weather would continue.

Unbeknownst to us at the time, the situation on board was becoming desperate, the crew sick and mutinous and the Captain forced to make a decision to try to sail on. It was a decision that pushed things firmly in our favour. I remember more than once that final day looking out of the door of *The Bull* and feeling the wind pick up, the sting of rain on my face, a crackle of something in the air that might have been lightning or might just have been a sense of anticipation that swelled and ebbed as we went about our daily business, the gang sharing the occasional secret sideways glance, wondering if the wind would ever change, and bring the *Amsterdam* in our direction.

Then finally the word came that she had lost her rudder in the storm and was drifting helpless, broken, in our direction. We hardly dared hope. Quite a crowd was gathering on the beach at Bulverhythe and we could see her, the tides pulling her closer and closer in towards the beach, the shriek of the wind and the creak of the broken ship in our ears, getting louder and louder until they mingled with the cries of the gulls and the shouts of the watching crowds as the stricken East Indiaman grounded and her keel was embedded in the soft sand. Then it was pandemonium as every one spilled onto the beach, helping the crew who were sick and under the influence of drink, having in their desperation broken into the ship's wine store. But wine was not all the *Amsterdam* was carrying, there being also a cargo of textiles, household goods, pens, pipes and a quantity of silver guilders – and before the night was out a proportion of those items had passed through our hands and vanished completely into the wet and windy night air, right under the noses of the authorities who were trying to take them into safe keeping. Indeed, at one point I saw John Cookson talking to a Customs Officer and I know, because I was watching, as I always watch, that his pockets were stuffed with shiny, silver coins.

And then it was over and I was back behind the bar of the *Bull Inn*, the place abuzz with talk, the excited chatter of people discussing the night's events. At one point conversation was so loud and animated that when John Cookson approached the bar, for once I felt I could safely speak to him without anyone overhearing. Even so, I still kept my voice low as I said, "Well, John, that's the easiest night's work we've had in a long while."
Anyone seeing him would've just put the burning light in his eyes, the almost feverish colour in his cheeks, down to a little bit too much to drink but of course, I knew better. Even so, he didn't let excitement overshadow caution as he leant on the bar and inclined his head towards me. "Aye, an easy night indeed, Miss Thomasina, an easy night indeed."

The Trifle

by Christine Cox

Squeezed into the pew with her brother and sisters, Noel fidgeted. Her faded velvet dress, which had first been her cousin's, and then her sister Ruth's, was too tight, and pinched under the arms; and her woollen stockings itched where they had been darned. Her hat, which Noel likened to an upside down chamber pot, had also been her cousin's, and seen better days. But her mother considered it Noel's best hat, the only one suitable for a daughter of the vicar to wear to church on Christmas Eve, even to the children's Crib Service.

The fidgeting earned a warning look from Miss Batley, the governess, and Noel almost scowled and fell into a sulk. Almost, but not quite: not today. There was plenty to scowl and sulk about, in addition to the clothes. The Sunday School children were performing a nativity play, and Noel was not in it: Noel, who was well known for her acting ability, and had been chosen for every children's play that had been put on since she was three years old. Last year, as Mary, she had ad-libbed a few words of her own. She had told the Angel Gabriel, who surprised her in the middle of her housework, "Don't you walk on my clean floor!" It had made the churchwardens laugh, but the Sunday School superintendent had not taken kindly to it, and this year Noel was banned. Today, though, there were also reasons to be joyful. It was Noel's tenth birthday. Her birthday was not usually much of an occasion, since everyone was too busy getting ready for Christmas to bother with special food or parties, and most of Noel's presents were combined ones, not received till the next day. But this year her mother had given her a beautiful green silk bow (concealed now under the chamber pot), which Noel had seen in a shop window and coveted for months. Annie, the new maid, who had taken a fancy to Noel, had made an enormous trifle for the children which did not have to be saved until the next day, but could be eaten after the third and most exciting reason to be joyful: a trip to the pavilion on the pier to see a Christmas show.

Noel had begged everyone not to tell her father about this luxurious dessert. The neighbourhood of St Peter's vicarage was a poor one, with high unemployment, and the Reverend Streatfeild was inclined to give away the family's scanty supply of food to any

17

hungry person who came begging. The Streatfeild parents were of noble descent, with a pedigree going back to the Norman invasion; but though they fulfilled the expectations of their class in sending their girls to Hastings and St Leonards Ladies' College and their son to Marlborough, employing a maid and a governess (for out of school supervision), and a cheap (therefore very bad) cook, they were poor as the mice that lived under the Reverend's pulpit, and depended on their gentleman farmer relatives for earthly sustenance.

Annie had obligingly covered the precious pudding with a plate and hidden it under some sacks on the larder floor, behind a crate of potatoes, and Noel felt it was safe. She boasted about it as the children and Miss Batley trooped down London Road and west along the sea front towards the pier, just opposite the Royal Victoria Hotel. There was a thin smattering of snow on the ground, not enough for it to be fun to play in, but enough to make the pavements slippery as the after-dark freeze set in. Noel had been allowed to abandon the chamber pot and cram her head into a woollen pixie hood, several sizes too small. She had somehow managed to smuggle her mother's moth-eaten fox fur out of the house without anyone noticing, and it now adorned her neck. Beside herself with excitement at the prospect of the show, she could not walk sedately, but gave little skips and jumps and twirls in time with the poem she was composing as she went:

My trifle, my trifle,
You should just get an eyeful!
With custard and cream,
As thick as a dream –

"It's not just *your* trifle," snapped her younger sister, Barbara. "It's for us too, you know. And take Mummy's fox fur off! She's going to kill you!" She grabbed at the fox fur, which came loose.

"It's so good, I could scream!" screamed Noel, attempting a pirouette on the icy pavement. The fox fur slid off and became entangled with her feet, and she fell into the neat privet hedge of one of her father's more respectable parishioners.

Miss Batley confiscated the fox fur. "For mercy's sake, Noel, if you cannot conduct yourself like a lady, we shall return home at once!" She sounded as if she meant this, and Noel tried to walk soberly the rest of the way, terrified of missing the show.

She managed it. Safely in her front row seat, she clapped wildly as a boy and girl came on stage. They were apparently called Henry and Eliza, and sang a song about a hole in a bucket. Henry was convincingly gormless, and Eliza satisfyingly disdainful, and the audience laughed. Even Miss Batley smiled. But the next song left the governess tutting. It was about a gentleman wanting to go milking with a milkmaid, and Batty clearly considered it improper, though Noel could not work out why. Noel was entranced by the whole show, from beginning to end, admiring the little actors, singers and ballerinas. Most especially she loved the last piece: the dance of the Sugar Plum Fairy. It was danced by a girl about Noel's own age; a slight and pretty girl (*unlike me,* thought Noel) dressed in layers of floaty, frothy pink, a silver tiara sparkling in her golden hair. *How wonderful to be able to dance like that! How wonderful!*

"Those children must have worked so hard," she said aloud as they set off back to the vicarage.

"Low class children!" Miss Batley sniffed. "Young ladies would never show their legs like that! And gentlemen's children do not travel the country putting on shows."

The governess clearly thought this outing had been a mistake on her employers' part. Though the children were encouraged to perform in amateur dramatics at home and at church, they were seldom taken to the theatre. Indeed, they had a great aunt who vowed never to visit such a place, for fear of dying there.)

'Low class,' to Noel, was a recommendation. Many times she had wished she could be a low class child, perhaps one who lived on a barge, or in a gypsy caravan, and didn't have to go to school, or learn collects on Sundays, or wear a chamber pot on her head. Fantasies of running away to join a troupe of travelling actors or dancers so occupied her mind all the way home that she forgot the trifle. It wobbled back into her head as they came up Cornfield Terrace and saw a group of ragged children loitering by the vicarage wall. These were low class children of the less fortunate sort: their parents out of work or drinking the money away. Noel had seen them before, begging by the station. *Well* she reassured herself, *Daddy can't have given them the trifle, or they'd have gone away.*

It had started to snow. Miss Batley hustled her charges indoors, but Noel hung back, intrigued by the eldest of the urchins, about the same age as herself and the Sugar Plum Fairy. As Noel turned to look, the girl caught her eye. Her face was thin, pale, grubby, but pretty, Noel thought, like the dancer's, and intelligent.

One of her brothers nudged the girl. "Ask 'er, Maggie, go on!"

His sister looked embarrassed, but stuck her chin out determinedly. "Spare a penny miss? Or something to eat?"

"We're 'ungry," added the boy.

Tomorrow would be Christmas: the one time of year when there was plenty to eat in the vicarage, because parishioners were always generous with their presents. This year the butcher had sent a ham and some sausages, the grocer a plum pudding, fancy biscuits and boxes of crystallised fruit. Uncle John had sent a fat goose, and Ruth had won a Christmas cake in a church raffle. Annie had baked mince pies. Suddenly, the trifle did not seem so important.

"Wait there!" Noel told the waifs, and went indoors.

"Hang up your wet things!" called Miss Batley. Noel obeyed, then stole quietly to the larder and opened the door. She pulled out the crate of potatoes and lifted the sacks. She removed the plate and admired her trifle, in all its glory. She ate the cherry that adorned the centre. She was entitled to that: it was her birthday. Then she carried the trifle carefully and quietly out to the children, using the scullery door so as not to attract attention.

The ragamuffins squealed with delight.

"You'd better eat it here," said Noel. "I need the bowl back. I'll get some spoons." But before she had finished speaking, the bowl was empty. The children had scooped up the pudding with their hands, and were licking the sticky remains off their fingers, along with the dirt.

That evening Noel was in trouble with her siblings for giving away their long-awaited treat; and with her mother too, who always, it seemed Noel, took other people's side against her. Barbara would not sleep in the bedroom they shared, and took herself off to find space in Ruth's bed. She was of the opinion that Noel had not given the trifle away, but secretly eaten it all herself, and would surely be very sick during the night.

20

Noel was not dismayed. The green silk bow, the dance of the Sugar Plum Fairy, and the gleeful cries of the hungry children before they wolfed down her trifle, had made this a wonderful birthday.

Noel took a pencil and exercise book from the bedside table, propped herself up in bed and wrote:

'Once upon a time there was a girl called Margaret who was very poor, but very pretty and clever. One day her fairy godmother...' *No, that was too babyish. A kindly teacher? A rich uncle, returned from the West Indies?* Wondering what benefactor should enable Maggie to become a famous dancer and rescue her family from poverty, Noel drifted off to sleep.

Biographical notes

Mary Noel Streatfeild was born on Christmas Eve 1895. She lived in St Leonards, at St Peter's Vicarage (now Streatfeild House care home), sandwiched between Cornfield Terrace and St Peter's Road, from 1902 to 1911. According to her fictionalised autobiography, *A Vicarage Family*, Noel felt herself to be a misfit; rebellious, misunderstood and overlooked, especially by her mother. She was expelled from Hastings and St Leonards Ladies' College (in Cumberland Gardens) at the age of fifteen, for organising a revenge campaign against a teacher she felt had wronged her. In at least one way Noel pleased her family, however. She was a talented actress, with the gift of making people laugh. She produced and took part in plays, humorous sketches and other entertainments in the parish,

21

some of which were devised as a distraction to keep the local populace from drinking and wife-beating.

As an adult, she acted in repertory theatre for several years before her career as a novelist began.

Noel wrote novels for adults, but the most famous are her children's stories. The first, *Ballet Shoes*, was published in 1936, and was followed by *Tennis Shoes, The Circus is Coming, Curtain Up, White Boots, Thursday's Child*, and many others.

'The Trifle' is a fictional story, but I have based it on the truth that Noel's writing was influenced by her admiration for some of the young performers she saw during her own childhood. She was impressed by their dedication and discipline. Disadvantaged children becoming dancers, sportspersons, skaters, actors etc, and raising themselves and their families out of hardship by their hard work and determination (sometimes eclipsing a more privileged rival) is a frequent theme in her writing. It is also true that St Leonards was afflicted by unemployment and poverty in the early twentieth century.

St Leonards pier was opened in 1891. It stood near the Royal Victoria Hotel, and was built on the initiative of the hotel proprietor. In 1900s it was taken over by an American company, and a roller-skating rink and pavilion were added. During the Second World War it was cut in half to prevent potential use by German invaders, fell into disuse, and was demolished in 1951.

Noel Streatfeild was awarded the OBE in 1983, and died in 1986, having published over sixty novels.

References

A Vicarage Family: a Biography of Myself by Noel Streatfeild (Peacock Books 1968); *Noel Streatfeild: a Biography* by Angela Bull (Collins 1984).

The Royal Wee

by Rosamond Palmer

Yesterday, on 29th April 2011, Queen Victoria's great, great, great, great, grandson got married, not that anyone thought of inviting her; she only knew the wedding was yesterday because she'd overheard passers-by talking about it, followed by the night revellers, staggering about aimlessly.

It was now two in the morning and a couple of wags filled what looked like a red and white dunces cap with beer, climbed onto her plinth and, hanging onto her royal personage, rammed the cap over her crown and lodged it in place.

Actually it didn't feel too bad; it fitted, after a fashion and at least it had some colour. Francis John Williamson had made her look so drab.

The alcohol trickled down her cleavage, permeating her bronze being, making her feel quite intoxicated, not to mention creating a pressing desire to visit the Ladies. She'd wanted to go since nineteen hundred and three and now it was urgent.

The same wags dumped a bucket of yellow paint under her pink marble plinth, with a view to touching her up.

"You get back up there and what you do is just pour it over her head."

"No, no, I want to be artistic."

Before she was able to sample this experience, one of those metal boxes on wheels, with a blue flashing light on the roof, came shrieking round the corner and the wags ran off.

Two men in black uniforms got out of the metal box and surveyed her new bonnet and the yellow paint.

"Can you see them?"

"No, they've legged it."

"The old girl smells like she's spent the night in a brewery."

"Is that beer, seeping out of that traffic cone?"

"I'm not climbing up there; we'll have to call the council."

"What about the paint?"

"Leave it; the council can deal with it."

They climbed back into their box and rode off.

24

Really, she hadn't had this much attention, since she'd been shot in the leg with a bullet from one of those tubes in the sky, during nineteen forty two!

Years of vibrating traffic had caused fractures in her structure. That shrieking metal box was the final straw; there was a creaking, cracking sound; Queen Victoria lurched forward. Her bodyweight peeled her feet off the plinth and she nose-dived into the paint. Mixed with the beer, its odour was quite obnoxious.

Her solid skirts meant her torso was angled towards the ground, squashing her nose. She rolled in one direction, then the other, feeling stiff and dented. Her legs clanged against her skirt. It was free. She tested its movement up and down, back and forth. The other leg creaked, shifted and bounced off her skirt, like a clapper striking a giant bell. Her frame reverberated and freed her arms.

She reached out and heaved herself towards the cobbles, bumped over them and struggled to the plinth. Then she pushed her sceptre into the ground and sprang off it. She gained a little height and as she fell back, rammed the sceptre into the marble plinth and rebounded upwards. One more bounce and she'd do it. This time, she nearly toppled over backwards and had to thrust her bodyweight forward. Then boing, clang, rattle, at last she came to rest in an upright position.

Finding her bearings, she then negotiated Grand Parade. Her skirts scraped the tarmac and sparks flew about both inside and outside her bronze frame. She knew where the Ladies Lavatories were; she'd been looking at the sign for many a decade. Could lavatories have changed? So many things had, like carriages, and what people wore.

Queen Victoria surveyed the yellow trail that evidenced her journey and giggled, "What a dreadful mess, worse than Bertie's bed sheets!"

And what a commotion, just to spend a penny. Did she have a penny? Did these modern people use pennies? She searched inside her lacy bag; it was empty. She'd been holding onto it for one hundred and eight years and for what? Nothing.

Then she lost her balance and bumped down the steps leading to the lower promenade. Fortunately, she landed in a vertical position and her dignity was restored though, truth to tell, she was so inebriated her dignity had escaped her.

Enjoying her freedom, she trundled along the prom to the Ladies. It was locked, and displayed a sign; Opening times 1st April-16th October 7am-9pm.

One hundred and eight years waiting, only to be met by a locked door. She was not amused. There was nothing for it; she'd have to go in the sea.

She bounced down the wooden steps onto the beach, pushing and crunching her heavy skirts through the shingle until she reached the refreshing waves. They lapped around her, slosh, slap, slosh. Finally, she was able to let go. Oh, what a relief.

Queen Victoria considered her return journey and decided she was better off where she was. She had always liked the sea and she couldn't think of a better place for the royal wee!

Secret Corners of St Leonards No 2

Artworks regularly appear in this secret corner. The one
in the photo is called "No Entry". Have *you* seen it?

The Warrior

by Steph Stonham

Calls in at Maureen's just now. Didn't stop long. Maximillian was in the front room, doing 'is flies. "You go on in, dear," Maureen said, "I'll bring you both a cup of tea in a minute."

As I went past the front room, I calls out, "'elloo, can't stop. Got an appointment."

I mean, fancy 'er asking me to go in there with 'im doing 'is flies. The brazen 'ussy. I guessed what type she was, soon as I saw 'er buying them black lace knickers in Debroyals. I never 'ad things like that to 'elp turn a man on, but then I didn't need 'em.

So I buys the paper an' comes in 'ere to read it. Sun's comin' out. If only that cold wind'd stop.

"Good afternoon, Queen Victoria. I hope you're comfortable up there." I wonder what she'd make of these two comin' along. The one wiv 'er skirt up her bum. What does she think she looks like! An' that watery lookin' youth wiv' 'er. What a pair! Throwing some bread to the pigeons. They'll only get the crumbs that's left. Like the working class. All in it together, are we? Except a few's at the top and the rest is at the bottom. What a raucous racket them gulls make when they's fightin' for food.

Raucous racket – that's good. I must put it in a letter one day.

There's a bit of a smell round 'ere. Someone's let their dog do its business. The police ought to do somethin' about it. But they won't, too busy ridin' round in comfy cars. I'm gonna move.

That's better. Oh my word, look what's comin' now. Totterin' along on them 'igh 'eels, an' she must be fifty if she's a day. Keeps on chewin' an' suckin'. I reckon she's gettin' raspberry pips out from between 'er teeth and spittin' 'em out.

It wasn't like this when I was young. No respect, that's what. No respect for themselves or anyone else. The 'ole country's goin' down the drain. That was one thing Victoria demanded – respect – "didn't you, Vicky?"

Now for the paper. 'atches, matches and dispatches first. It used to be about me friends gettin' married, an' havin' children, now it's all about them dyin'.

Oh no, it's Bertie – died last week of an 'eart attack. Dear ol' Bertie, I remember when him and me... no, better not go down that road, seems disrespectful like. Still, 'e never 'ad a weak 'eart in them days. Like a two stroke engine 'e was when I got 'im all fired up.

What's this? Disgraceful! I must say the council's pretty free with our money. They'll be paying consultants to sort out the consultants next.

I'll check the letters page now, take my mind off poor ol' Bertie... Yes, 'ere's mine! I knew it was good enough to print.

Hastings.uk.com

We've got miles of chilly prom
Fish n chips
And freezing dips.
Short skirts – I call them belts
Must be the cut-backs, I've no doubt.
Our peerless pier – can it be saved
Or should it sink back beneath the waves?
In spite of all it is my home
Far from it I do not roam.
– the Worrier of Warrior Square

Not bad, if I do say it meself. Bertie wouldn've laughed. I'll push it through Maureen's letterbox on me way home.

Sun's gone in. I might as well go 'ome and watch a bit of telly in the warm.

Bye bye, Victoria, see you tomorrow. 'ave you noticed the plants all regimented, afraid to step out of line? You would've liked that, I expect. Well, all I can say is…

I am not amused!

Secret Corners of St Leonards No 3

You probably recognise Burton's Clock (left) but do you know where to find the other one (below)?

A Palette of Stones

by Victoria Seymour

Sid Beynon Image © 2012 Juliette Dodd

It could be said that Sid Beynon was a successor to the sand artists, who in the early part of the 20th century, literally scratched a living on Hastings' then sandy beaches. In the mid-1990s, Sid was riding his bicycle along the seafront, when he spotted the name Paul, picked out in brown pebbles on the beach. This inspired Sid to experiment with his own beach pebble designs and a natural, artistic talent emerged. In his untutored hands, the sea-smoothed pebbles; grey-blue, brown, red, white, and black, were formed into images of sea creatures, wild animals, historical and legendary characters and mystical symbols.

As Sid worked he was oblivious to the fact that he was being watched by local resident, Rosemary Chennery, who suggested to him that he should apply for an Arts Foundation Course. Sid, who loved to tell friends how he left school at the age of 12 with nothing more than four swimming certificates, was accepted at Hastings

College of Arts and Technology and began the Foundation Course in August 1998, where he began to draw for the first time.

He continued to produce beach art, by then in the company of two friends, Jamie Stapeley and Paul Garrett. Sid's work became more complex and he built up a repertoire of designs, gaining a reputation as a beach entertainer. Crowds gathered to watch him work; children joined him on the beach, imitating his creations; some onlookers threw coins in appreciation. Along with his growing interest in beach art, Sid began to develop a new personal philosophy. The timeless quality of the beach influenced him and when he spoke about this environment you could sense that for him it was a living entity. The difficulties of his early life fell into perspective; tolerance pervaded his thinking.

One of his most treasured possessions was a scruffy exercise book, which he used to hang on the promenade railings, so that spectators could write comments on his work. The book was filled with praise for his pictures from local people and visitors from all over the world. Sid struck up a special rapport with Hastings' young skateboarders and BMX riders, who used the cycle track on the promenade. Asked how he felt about the vandals who occasionally demolished his work, he said that he thought it was better that they vent their frustration on beach stones rather than on people or valuable possessions.

In 1999, Sid was accepted as a student at the University of Wales Institute, Cardiff, and completed a three-year course for a BA Honours in Fine Art. He began working with other materials and the natural talent he used with pebbles was expanded into other fields. The value of his work became recognised, particularly as a route into design for would-be artists of all ages, but especially for children. He participated several times as an outdoor artist in the Rother Community Summertime Arts programme. His enthusiasm and modest approach to his work made him the perfect tutor for children or those who lacked artistic experience.

He eventually became a key figure at Hastings Arts Forum Gallery, based in St Leonard's. Chairman of the HAF Harry Lyons said: "Sid was a cornerstone of the Hastings Arts Forum. He joined during 2006, as the forum was acquiring its two galleries and was seldom absent, administering the busy schedule of constantly changing shows."

A typically reticent photo-shoot –
Sid on the steps of Hastings Arts Forum

In August 2010, at the age of 54, Sid Beynon died from a heart attack, two days before his first ever show was set to start. His death was mourned throughout the local art community and friends held a beach-front memorial service. On 15th September St Ethelburga's Church at St Leonards was filled to capacity when nearly 200 mourners gathered to pay their respects. The simple coffin, of unvarnished wood, was inscribed with designs and words from his family and friends. After a committal at Hastings Crematorium, a wake was held at Azur, on the edge of the beach that was Sid's early work place.

In October 2011 a memorial to Sid, in the form of a commemorative plaque and mosaic, was unveiled on the St Leonard's seafront. The mosaic, designed by local portrait artist Juliette Dodd, constructed from beach pebbles, is a dolphin, one of Sid's most popular beach designs. The stones for the piece were gathered by Mike Williams, under the guidance of Sid's friend Jamie Stapeley. The plaque reads: "Sid Beynon, 1956-2010, Beach Artist, The beach is my studio, the stones are my palette." After the memorial was unveiled, children took part in a workshop making mosaics on the beach.

Hastings Borough Council announced that Sid will be remembered with a street name on a new development. A section of road at the top of Elphinstone Road will be officially called Beynon Way. The Arts Forum's Harry Lyons said that he was delighted to see the town recognise the life of one of its most colourful sons.

A piece of Sid's work that was not widely seen was his attempt to create a line of large pebbles, running from Hastings Pier to the Harbour Arm, in the few hours that the tide reveals the sandy stretch of the beach. The event featured in an amateur video; it made hypnotic viewing. As Sid and his helpers bent to gather stones under a cloudy dawn, a few early dog walkers stopped to wonder at the process. The silence was broken only by the faint sound of waves from a calm sea, the cry of seagulls and the click of stone on stone. The scene symbolised the peace and dedication that pervaded Sid's artistic years.

'Nothing is written in stone' © Sid Beynon, 2002

Secret Corners of St Leonards No 4

Here's a lovely place for a spot of lunch along with some local art and info... but where is it?

Poetry Group

by Tony Frost

There are deep undercurrents at Hastings Arts Forum
In dark little corners, you shouldn't ignore 'em.
It's true that photographers, painters in oil,
Deft sculptors and craftsmen in clay with their toil
Intellectually speaking are filling the gap
In the landscape and putting the town on the map.
But for some restless thinkers with masses to say
On the human condition, there's no other way
But to wrestle the problem of man's earthly yoke
With a finely honed sonnet or well-rhyming joke.

Some scribblers are fired by poets long gone,
Others dash off ideas as the bus trundles on
And it may be an ode from a moment of sadness,
Sue's wails on a boyfriend who drove her to madness,
But Mavra, non-poet until she got going,
Spouts eloquent wit, now they can't stop her flowing
And even the Chairman, whose voice was unheard,
Gamely rolled up his sleeves, penned some powerful words.
But the guy at the back, when his fingers get itchy,
Is vastly more funny when his poems are bitchy.

So it all gets thrown into a poetic soup
Which is served up and savoured each month by the group.
You can't tell what comes next, may not know what it means,
Could be solemn or jokey or somewhere between.
But get down to the Arts Forum once in a while,
Hear our very best metaphors, crafted with style.
Shun the Saturday throng, supermarkets and strife
And just ponder with us the true meaning of life.
For a book lies within every soul as we know
But there's poetry too – you should give it a go.

Mavra

by Tony Frost

There's a lady I know from St Leonards-on-Sea
who's becoming the artist she long craved to be
and she seems pretty normal to judge by her face,
She's not weird or insane and both ears are in place,
But her metamorphosis to friends is a shock
For she's churning out artworks you really can't knock.
She's so clever with brushes and pastels and pencils
And socking great rubbers and rulers and stencils
And all the devices which help you to draw
That the fruits of her labours will leave you in awe.
From a lifetime of stabbing at typewriter keys
She's now smothered in charcoal from forehead to knees
And you'd better not greet her and stop for a talk
Or your hand will get covered in graphite or chalk.

So her fingers which had such a dexterous touch
And made QUERTY spew letters and memos and such
Capture humans or creatures with masterful strokes
Or a twist of her knife or a carefully-judged poke.
Now her staircase and landing are plastered with cats,
Some are slinky or jokey and some are plain bats,
But her parlour is papered with all kinds of nudes
Which are highly curvaceous but not at all rude.
She can even turn crones with deep wrinkles and lumps
Into elegant ladies with beautiful bumps.
But her fingers are feverish, aching to draw
Every subject in sight and considerably more,
So it's wise to keep moving, don't pause for a minute
Or else she'll start drawing and, mate, you'll be in it.

Mavra the Hat

by Tony Frost

Mavra the Hat is a variable soul
And the style of her headgear expresses just that,
For from Monday to Sunday you really can't guess
If it's going to be striking or floppy or flat.

She has dozens of titfers in red, blue and grey,
Even purple and pink and they're more often caps,
But they differ in many extraordinary ways,
Denim, canvas or cord and I think some have flaps.

Now she claims that her colourful headgear is donned
To protect her dark eyes from the sunshine and such,
But I'm sure it's the Mavra inside that she guards,
For in Mavra there's mystery, in hats there's not much.

Bar Blah

by Tony Frost

Eddie's sitting in the corner
On a pouffé sipping beer
Whilst I watch and feel the rhythm
Of the crowd who brought me here.

Tall gent in a well-cut jacket,
Trilby tilted to the right,
Holds his tall glass like a woman,
Gazes out into the night.

Smart young redhead in a dark suit
And a blonde in flowery top,
Gesturing when words are failing,
Urgent lest the fun should stop.

Eddie's joking with a black man,
Eyes of coal and gentle hands.
Next to him a jean-clad artist
Restless as the shifting sands.

Black and white and every colour
Find a refuge in this place,
Pausing from the long day's motion,
Tired of hand and lined of face.

Here's a forum for the talker
And the guy who's left his wife.
Here's a harbour for the wanderer
And the man escaping life.

Here you'll slow down to earth's tempo,
Find peace if the mood is right.
Here you'll find old friends or new ones,
Taste the freedom of the night.

Secret Corners of St Leonards No 5

The Secret Gardens

by Delia Ann Green

There are public gardens in St Leonards that are quite hard to find
You enter through an archway and the gardens are right behind.
They're just glimpsed from the pavement
– you can hardly see them there
But once in the gardens you can only stand and stare

At the emerald grass, the bushes, flowers and trees
The shimmering lake with ducks gliding elegantly among the leaves
Causing ripples between the lilies they all know
Whilst big fish skim though the water down below.
Dogs on leads try to break free and run away
And young children laugh, and shout as they play
But when the people and dogs have all gone home
It's such a tranquil place in which to roam
And there's a bonus in this hidden gem too
For in the background, the sea's in view.
Trees, a lake, winding paths among shrubs and flowers
We should be proud of these gardens of ours.

The Business with the Pier

Photo copyright © 2012 Zelda Chappel

The View from St Leonards

by Angela Perkins

My stepbrother, Francis, takes off his sunglasses, peers critically at the view in front of him and says, "We came all that way for this?"

Brian says, "If you count about 25 miles as 'all that way'," then yes, we did. Anyway, you didn't have to come."

Francis makes a face at him and says accusingly, "Kit said we were going to Hastings. This isn't Hastings."

I roll my eyes because although he's 26 he's got a talent for behaving like an eight-year-old. I point into the distance and say, "That side is Hastings, this side is St Leonards-on-Sea. We've got to be on this side; the light's all wrong looking at it the other way at this time of day. Anyway there's some shops I want to look in later; St Leonards is gaining quite an artistic community."

Francis says, "Well so it might be, but it hasn't got much of a pier."

Brian gives me the ghost of a wink because he pretty much knows that Francis is going to start winding me up at any moment and he's used to playing peacemaker. He says, "Well actually, St Leonards hasn't got any pier at all; its remains were demolished in 1951. That's Hastings Pier that you're looking at. How far do you want to walk along, Kit?"

I squint into the distance. "Not much further I don't think, or else we'll be too close. What's that statue?"

Brian peers at the map. "That's Warrior Square and the statue is Queen Victoria, although in all the pictures I've seen of her, this is the first time I've seen her wearing a traffic cone for a hat. Is that the influence of your artistic friends do you think?"

I reflect that even when I'm determined to be in a bad mood, he invariably manages to break through it and in spite of myself I laugh. "More likely the sort of thing Francis would do after a night out."

Francis puts on a look of comic outrage, although I suspect its actually just the sort of thing he'd do, particularly as he doesn't actually deny it, he just says instead, "So exactly why are we here?"

We've come to some steps now and I turn to go down them towards the beach, the pier silhouetted against the sky. I jump down onto the pebbles, point towards it and say simply, "I want to paint it."

44

He says, "Darling, it needs way more than a coat of paint." He might be my stepbrother, but he can be extremely annoying at times.

"Shut up," says Brian, who knows when I'm getting near my limit.

But I'm hardly listening, I'm already setting off down the beach, the pebbles crunching and sliding beneath my feet. I stop about half way down and, even before I sit down, I'm slipping the messenger bag off my shoulder. Although the day is bright, there's a chill in the wind and I put up my sweatshirt hood, more to keep my hair out of my eyes than anything. I pull my sketchpad and a pencil out of the bag and start, almost urgently, to make a rough sketch.

Francis says, "Couldn't you have got a picture off the internet or something?"

I shake my head and say, slightly breathlessly, "I needed to feel it."

He says, "Feel it? I can tell you what it feels like, a lot of metal and some charred wood."

I stop drawing for a second to stare at him in disbelief. I always manage to forget that not everyone sees things the way I do. I say, "You can't feel its heart, its soul from a photograph."

He gives a little snort. "Heart and soul? It's not alive you know."

I decide I can draw and talk at the same time so without looking up I say, "It was."

Francis spreads his hands out in front of him in a sort of *non comprendo* gesture and I say, "Can't you imagine it when it was first built? I mean I can't remember exactly when ..."

Brian says quickly, "1872," then looks slightly embarrassed. "Sorry, I was reading about it last night; I've just got a stupidly retentive memory."

I'm amused because I was reading it too but I've got a terrible memory for dates. "1872 then, but can you imagine it? It was a very wet and windy day but thousands of people still came out for the opening and lined the route to the pier from the station where the Earl of Granville arrived for the opening. All the route was decorated with flags and when they declared it open there was a gun salute from a steam yacht and all the people clapped and cheered despite the rain." I pause to get a softer pencil out of the bag. "Then there was a grand dinner in the Pier Pavilion, and in the evening a concert and fireworks."

Brian leans forward. "'The peerless Pier', the Earl of Granville called it. You're right Kit, it really must have really been something to see."

"Imagine the noise," I say, "the colour, the feeling of pride that day, the feeling of being alive."

Brian says, "A few years later a landing stage was added and steamers used to take people on boat trips. That must have been quite a sight."

I nod. "They added all sorts of buildings and bits to it over the next few years, but then it burnt down."

Francis lifts his sunglasses, gives me a look, and says, "So I see."

Brian laughs. "No, no, it first burnt down in 1917, but it was rebuilt, even better than before."

I flip over a page in the book and draw a quick sketch from memory from a photograph I saw on the internet and say, "By 1930 they'd even added an Art Deco frontage to it."

Brian peers over my shoulder and looks impressed – but he might just be impressed I remembered the date. He lays back on the pebbles, looking up at the clouds, even though it's probably a bit chilly for sunbathing, and says, "Just as well they built it at the front really, in 1938 the other end suffered storm damage."

Francis says, "Blimey, its had a hard life hasn't it?" He suddenly realises what he's said. "Oh great Kit, now you've got me doing it." He puts his hand up to shield his eyes from the sun. "I'm probably going to regret this," he says, "but go on then, what happened next?"

Brian says, "Well, the War started a year later and the pier was closed and used for training. Plus it was deliberately broken at the shore end to prevent the Germans using it for a landing stage."

Francis says, "Doing its bit for the war effort; very noble."

I'm doodling in the corner of my second page now: falling bombs and smoke behind the Art Deco façade, "And paying for it – it suffered bomb damage."

Francis, who is looking decidedly more cheerful than he did earlier says, "Don't tell me, I can guess, then it was rebuilt again."

Brian grins at him. "You're catching on. Do you know, in the 60s and 70s artists like The Who, Genesis and Jimi Hendrix played there?" He sits up and, with the air of someone throwing a dog a tasty biscuit, he says, "Even Pink Floyd," because he knows they're one of Francis's favourites.

I say, "You think riots are something new? There was even fighting around the pier in 1964 between Mods and Rockers."

Brian sits up. "But the last decade or so have been the hardest of all. Between then and the present day it changed hands several times until it was finally closed over fears of safety. There were ongoing talks about what should happen to it, but these things move so slowly, that nothing was finalised. A sad state of affairs for a grand old lady."

Francis is sitting now with his knees drawn up, his elbows resting on them and his chin resting on his interlocked fingers. He's looking at the pier through slightly narrowed eyes, obviously aware that that's not the end of the story. "Go on," he says.

Brian shifts uncomfortably on the pebbles, shrugs slightly and says, "In the early hours of October 5th last year there was a massive fire; fire fighters battled it from the land end and from the sea but parts of it were still smouldering several days." He gestures towards the pier. "And here it is, a year later."

I say, "That pier has been here through the lifetime of everyone who lives in this town. Can you imagine seeing that in front of you every time you walk down St Leonards seafront and then one day it being gone, pulled down or fallen down or just slipped into the sea because of apathy or lack of money or whatever? All that history, all that *life* just gone?"

Brian smiles at the fervour in my voice and says, "Its so easy isn't it, just to get used to seeing something and not to give it a second thought until you've lost it."

Francis looks thoughtful. "It looks like some kind of skeleton. So that's it? After all that, this is the end?"

Brian shakes his head. "There's a lot of people working very hard behind the scenes to secure funding so there's still hope."

We sit in silence for a moment, and somehow the sound of the traffic seems to fade into the distance until all I can hear is the wind and the occasional mournful cry of the gulls. And with the others watching me, with a few quick strokes I draw a towering bird rising from the skeleton structure: a phoenix rising from the ashes.

Image copyright © 2012 Gloria Dean

Photo copyright © 2012 Zelda Chappel

Hastings Pier (fire)

by Zelda Chappel

Not yet struck two on the southern coast,
and a thrill creeps in under commotion's guise
to a place where chaos is a stranger.
Sirens, silent but blue, pour out onto streets
and in through our windows in a quiet panic

while curtains twitch to grab a glimpse
of the bitter orange dance.
Charcoal throws itself to the night,
and realisation follows quick and blunt:
death is devouring the icon on the sea front.

This is the end. As metal bends,
and wood breaks and splinters and falls
down beneath the waves,
no man nor boat can save her at all.
And the devil keeps dancing in the sky,
the wind standing back and keeping an eye

until the morning sun breaks through September
air charred and heavy in its smoky haze.
Clouds cover bones laid bare and stark,
dark and bleeding rusty red, looking strange
in their folding in and in and in on themselves.

While the sea rages, trying to soften the edges
with its blows, it leaves her carcass strewn
across the pebbles, thrown into empty muscle shells,
half broken with blackened carbon lines
all ragged and jagged and sore.

The Pier's Tale

as told to Gloria Dean

(Page 48) above is a watercolour impression of what happened to me on the night of the 5th October, 2009. The days have passed since then, and I am still as I was the following morning. But not without Hope, oh no! What happened then has passed away and when I am renewed, I will add the trauma of that night to my memory bank.

This bank of mine goes back a long way. It contains events both good and bad – as memories do – but I won't become maudlin and try to recount even some of the incidents of my life but will choose just one of many vivid days. Now let me see... it involves going back some way. I have chosen a joyous occasion. Wednesday, 6th April 1927. Many of you may wonder what happened. Some, from the older generation, will remember.

From early in the morning an excited crowd began to assemble along the entire sea front, stretching as far as West St Leonards Station. There were very many women and children, dressed in clothes unfamiliar to you today. The ladies were feminine, and good to look at; the little girls in frocks and the boys dressed as boys. All of the youngsters were noisily happy but controlled, and kept with their parents.

People gathered especially numerously in front of me but I wasn't the object of their interest. I didn't mind. I had the best view of anyone there. I could feel excitement vibrating throughout my frame. The jostling, the chattering, the shrills of impatient children.

We had to wait until 11.10am. Everyone strained forward. I remained immobile as always. The increased shouting surrendered to cheering, and then to frantic flag-waving. Someone of great importance was passing by in a cavalcade of immaculate cars. Who?

I heard a name. Edward, the Prince of Wales, no less. Darling of the country. *The Prince of Wales!*

He passed by in an instant. The noise of the crowd lowered into a contented resonance. More activity followed. The Prince was to return to the newly completed White Rock Pavilion standing right across the road from myself. A Guard of Honour was being formed (apparently, it was the third if His visits to Hastings on that day.)

At 11.35am, the uproar of cheers and devoted goodwill rose again. His Royal Highness alighted, inspected the Guard and then graciously disappeared into the pristine Pavilion to perform the Opening Ceremony, an act accompanied by the National Anthem, the Mayor's Speech, the Choir rendering *Jerusalem* and the concluding prayer delivered by the Right Reverent Bishop of Lewes.

Then, yet another upsurge of affection and patriotism – The Prince – this good-looking young man – came onto the Pavilion balcony overseeing the extended promenade. How the women in the crowd loved him. You talk about celebrity mania these days! This man surpassed them all but his admirers were more contained and without the abandon of today's worshippers. It was much nicer to see, I can tell you.

Edward then left the Pavilion to continue his Programme. I saw no more of him. The crowd, no doubt, moved to other points along his route. They left behind a haze of love and civic pride. Hastings and its grand neighbour were grand places, yes.

The Pavilion began its duties that very night with the first concert of the Hastings Musical Festival. There were to be four concerts in four days, with guest conductors including Mr Edward German, Mr Basil Cameron (also Musical Director of the whole Festival) Sir Edward Elgar OM, and Sir Henry Wood. Artistes ranged from Miss Carrie Tubb (lovely name) suprano, to the world famous pianist Pouishnoff.

Ticket prices were 7/6d, 5/9d, 4/9d, 3/6d and 2/4d. Series tickets (four concerts) at 24/0d, 18/0d, 15/0d, 12/0d. Seats bookable at 10 Verulam Place, Hastings.

Conductor Sir Henry, soloist Pousihnoff: I strained to listen and tried to absorb the beauty of the music. I hoped that its glory would enter my structure, to sustain and uplift me in any future times of stress, should it ever come.

Well it certainly did, and lasted a while, culminating a year ago through the destroying hands of thoughtless young men.

I refuse to take on a pitiful tone. There was even dramatic beauty in the flames that consumed me. Since then, I have remained as you see me, skeletal and gaunt, waiting for loyal people of Hastings and St Leonards to resurrect me. It may take time, but until then I give you one of my tales – a happy recollection.

I am content.   *Your Pier*

A Picture Perfect History of Hastings

by Samantha Young

Photo © 2012 Samantha Young

Samantha remembers Hastings Pier as a place her late Granddad used to enjoy fishing, and sends us these photos to remind us that the pier is not the only attraction to have been lost to vandalism of one kind or another. "Childhood memories were visually gone," she said, as she stood on the hill in the White Rock Gardens looking down on the remains of the pier.

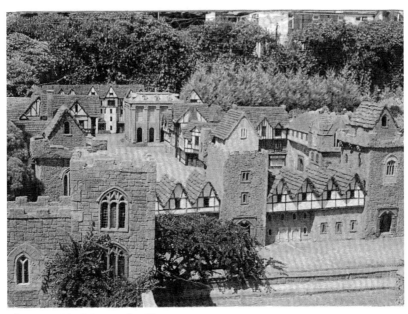

photo © 2012 Samantha Young

Welcummy To St Loonies-On-Sea

On brilly springy mornigs like these
when the sunflakes tinkle over the
promprom, come all cardybeiges
(armyarm with your hubbyytrusses)
and wimp and womber beside the
peacy seasy. You will find the folksies
a delighter!

All drunksy are the no-no-hopes as they grum and gabber and
fiddlydoo with their foreshores. Nah! Weepy not at the gigant
quantit of "effs" and "bees" nor mournsy the cohorts of beggies,
buggies, stealies and narkies. But dimble down to the historiantic
booseyholeys and be welcummy by the local lonedopes, where you'll
find an apres-ski that's oft pissed.

Thus, after your visitate, you
will regurge to the Big
Metrop all refreshered and
reflattened, your mentals full
of the airy salters and the
sheety breezers, not to
mention the psychopathetic
inhabitates.

Come again! But, gawdelpyer, not eary deary!

(*This is a collavatory work by Anthony Frost, Reuben Ramsay and
H. Wyndham Davidson*)

Wyndham's Cartoon

I'm fed up, frankly really miffed,
For Wyndham with a wicked laugh
Pulled out a big cartoon and said
He saw me as a tall giraffe.

It's true my long legs lope around
In Hastings town at faster pace
Than Wyndham when his bet's come in
Or was he looking at my face?

That awful thought impels my eyes
Downwards to the cartoon's corner
Where jovial Tim is bouncing out
In no way like sedate Jack Horner!

But yes, Tim's known across the town
For stripy jumpers, well-worn style,
And baggy shorts, also a nose
That smells old records at ten miles.

But leftwards little Wyndham lurks
In jacket, shirt and air force tie.
He hates his Royal Terrace rooms
But penguins simply cannot fly!

Tony Frost

Cartoonist
H Wyndham Davidson

55

HWD

Mountain Girl

by Tony Frost

To Riju, from Nepal, working at SPAR in St Leonards-on-Sea.

You bid me write a poem for you
But who can conjure words with grace,
Gaze on a stranger and discern
What passions burn within the face?

Have I the artist's eye to see
The shadow that hides behind the veil
And with my sable brush disclose
The soul that struggles to prevail?

I see your dark impassive eyes
From far-off lands and snow-clad slopes.
Only my intuition tells
Of half-glimpsed sorrows, cherished hopes.

Sometimes, not often, I can see
That on your brow a furrow lies
Until the sunburst of your smile
Breaks through grey Himalayan skies.

Who knows what trials or nomad dreams
Led you to tread our English shores
And brought your mountain wisdom here
To breeze through drab suburban doors?

The Man From Nepal

by Tony Frost

There's a man in the SPAR shop
Who comes from Nepal,
But he's not a fierce Gurkha,
Not warlike at all.
If you make a mistake
When you pay for your bread,
He'll just smile very broadly,
Not shoot you stone dead.

Now I've heard that the Germans
Despaired for their lives
When the Gurkhas came charging
With funny-shaped knives,
But he won't cut your throat
If you query the change.
He's a peaceable guy,
Not the least bit deranged.

When the loonies and tramps
From St Leonards-on-Sea
Try to pocket a Mars bar
Or get some beer free,
He's not really that bothered
To see the clots caught,
For he's calm as a sadhu
Who knows life is short.

He won't wave a khukūri
Or call up the Law,
For he's really too genial
And finds it a bore.
So it's no use at all
Getting stroppy or riled,
For you can't pick a fight
With a guy who just smiles.

An Introduction to the Biography of Alex Ntung

I originally come from DRC (Congo), from a nomadic tribe of cattle herders called Banyamulenge or Congolese Tutsi. My great grandparents came from Rwanda and moved to the pre-colonial Congo searching for good pastures. Because of our cultural background and perceived physical features, we have been racially excluded and persecuted in Congo. I came to Britain fleeing persecution in DRC, a country that has endured political and social turmoil since gaining independence from Belgium in 1960: secessionist war, different rebellions, and three decades of authoritarian rule. In this tragic journey, my community was singled out and forced to leave DRC. From 1996 to 1998 more than six African nations and a dozen rebel groups have been involved in the conflict, which grew into one of the cruellest tragedies of the 20th century. I was one of many who experienced this extremely challenging journey. I lost 11 relatives (uncles, brothers and cousins) before I fled, ironically, to Rwanda, a country that had just experienced a genocide in which a million people were killed in a hundred days.

As soon as I arrived in the UK I claimed asylum, but was detained for three days at one of the London airports (which I realised later was Gatwick.) Then I was picked up by security officers and brought to a place called Hounslow, where I spent seven days before being sent to St Leonards. As I did not speak English I had no idea what their plans or intentions were. Journeys from one place to another were terrifying. I lived in constant fear that they might be taking me back.

Coming to St Leonards, I was picked up by a tall and strong security man. He had so many keys and belts around him, I thought we were heading for a prison. The van/minibus windows were partly tinted so I could hardly see out. The driver stopped so many times to pick up other asylum seekers. The only location that I clearly remember was a very busy place which took my breath away. It was near the sea and I could see ships, and so many cars. Later, I realised it must have been the port of Dover.

No-one in the van could speak English, so we couldn't communicate with each other. Arriving in St Leonards, we were handed over to another security team and I was offered a room to share with two boys from Sudan. It was in the former Adelphi Hotel. Faced with the apparently solid square of buildings surrounding Warrior Square Gardens, with the railings and sea beyond, I thought they were some sort of enclosure, so that we couldn't escape. I had seen islands in Africa designed for detention, and thought this was something similar. It was two months before I realised that beyond Warrior Square was a town, and we could actually move about freely. The letter from the UK Border Agency ordering us to 'reside at the address given and to report to the police when required', didn't mean we were imprisoned.

My time at Adelphi was difficult psychologically as we were the authorities' responsibility and had to make contact regularly with professional agencies: the security team at Adelphi and other support and enforcement services. I constantly worried what would be happening the next day. We had to check our mail every day to see whether we had been granted permission to stay in the UK. There were between 150 and 250 asylum seekers at the hotel, mainly from Iraq, Afghanistan, Angola, Zimbambwe, Sudan, DRC and Tchad, all in the same limbo.

Luckily, I was issued a work permit three months later – but not a residency permit. I managed to register at a language school. Despite culture and language barriers and my own personal background, after six months of learning English I decided to look for a job, but I didn't know how to go about it. A man in a big car came to the Adelphi and I found out that he was offering work. I asked him whether he could give me a job. The next day, he came for me and some other asylum seekers. It was a removal job. We worked from 9am to midnight, completing a removal from a massive house in Brighton and making a start on two other houses near Bexhill. We went on to do many more, in a place that looked like a big city, over the course of five days, 14 hours a day. For all that effort, I was paid £25. I was shocked, and told the man I was quitting, he kept saying 'this is England', persuading us that it was naïve to think life would be easy, and that quitters were losers. He said nobody would ever give us a job, and that asylum seekers' work was restricted if we had a work permit – and he threatened to report us! I argued as best I could with my little English, saying that a work permit is a work permit, and should not have restrictions. Like the others, I was very angry but did not know what to do.

My second job was with another man who came to pick us up (me and four friends). He said he was offering a very good job. He started by asking if we could communicate on radios, and before we answered he said he could train us. I thought he sounded like a genuine businessman, and different from the last one. He drove us a few hours away, to a large park full of music stages. To this day I don't know where it was but I guess that it was the WOMAD festival. He took us to register and gave us security badges, introducing us as 'professional security staff' then deployed us to various stages around the large festival site. Each of us was given a uniform and allocated a very long square-shaped pillar with a chair on top, so we could see what was going on throughout the grounds. We started work at about 8am; the man did not turn up at lunch time, nor in the evening so no breaks – I only managed a toilet break because there happened to be one near my pillar.

Around 10pm, I radioed to two friends who spoke Swahili. 'I feel dizzy,' I said, 'and hungry, and I am desperate to leave.' They were in the same state, so we went to the festival security office, where they told us we'd been recruited by an agent and weren't their responsibility, and that we should go back to our duty as soon as possible.

We stayed until morning and on into the next day with no sign of relief. The next evening I radioed my friends again, and we decided to quit, but we were very hungry and weak, and didn't know how to get back to St Leonards. We went to sleep in a tent but it was very cold, so two hours later we decided to go and look for a train station. We had no ticket money but we saw a train coming and decided to try it. That was my very first time travelling in a train. It all seemed so sophisticated. By and by, we arrived at the London Underground – another new experience. We got through all the barriers by begging security to let us pass, explaining our predicament.

One man was very kind. He explained the route and gave us a little note like a pass to show at the next stations. He bent the rules to provide a humane service. I still appreciate his support not just because of his kindness but because he understood the predicament of asylum seekers, that they exist not even on the periphery of society. Their journey to residency means being forced into a life of penury. To be an asylum seeker is to live a life full of barriers and limited awareness of their rights and entitlements. It is about being in a limbo that is either invisible to, or ignored by, those who have secure tenure. It is also a life of fear of being deported. My friends and I never got paid for that job, and never heard from the man who hired us, despite many phone calls to 'his office'.

My third job was more structured. It was at a chicken factory in Uckfield – an extremely cold place – the work was very hard. We were processing dead chickens by hand, packing them for distribution. I had to set out at 4am to start work at 5.30, finishing at 4pm, after which I attended my evening courses. It was my first salary, and I bought a computer to help me with my studies. As my English got better, my awareness grew of the range of difficulties that newcomers to Hastings face, difficulties that could only be solved by better social integration and cultural awareness. I started an organisation to support these newcomers and to challenge the media that portray the wrong information, which attracts the wrong attention from the wrong kind of people. By this time I was becoming very protective towards the St Leonards area. It was the first place that I had ever felt safe. I wanted to look after the facilities the area offers: the sea and the park and the local residents who made it all so peaceful. I decided to leave the Adelphi. I did not like being given free (but monotonous) meals. I now had a salary and I did not need asylum support services. Even though my residency permit was still not settled and in fact was becoming a problem, I decided to rent a studio flat. At this point I had no idea it was going to take another three years and many court appeals before I was granted residency.

St Leonards has always been a safe place for me: Hastings and St Leonards has been a dispersal area for asylum seekers for the last twelve years but there has never been any violence or conflict between local residents and asylum seekers. Despite negative media coverage, St Leonards residents were very welcoming and helpful. A few felt that we were 'an issue' but still we were relatively safe. I was worried though, to hear that people think there is a problem.

I applied to the Hastings Trust for a small fund to organise a multicultural festival in Warrior Square Gardens, I organised performances by asylum seekers from different countries to promote cultural diversity and a positive image of migrants. I also managed to get some professional cultural performing groups from surrounding areas to join the festival. We had support from local residents; the event was attended by more than 1500 people. I was very honoured to welcome the local MP and other the agencies that came to support us. It was an emotional time for me as I needed to send a message that, contrary to widespread information, we were in St Leonards to bring something new and positive.

The following year, I managed more funding and organised the same cultural events at two locations (Warrior Square Gardens and White Rock Theatre). A year later, with more resources, St Leonards Festival was initiated and established by the local residents and this was going to be in Warrior Square Gardens: this had an even more creative cultural programme that brought together people from different backgrounds. I was asked to manage one of the festival stages on Kings Road.

As my English had improved a lot, I managed to get a job in a care home, I enjoyed this work very much because I had opportunities to help and speak to elderly people who shared a similar life experience – of war, in the Second World War.

The impact of asylum seekers, combined with the enlargement of the EU in recent years, has meant that the area is rapidly changing, demographically. Incomers have brought a range of valuable skills and experience: resources that have been of great benefit to local business and industry. Although the majority moved from St Leonards as it was perceived as having no job opportunities, others have continued their studies and moved on into professional jobs – teachers, nurses, electricians, IT technicians – in the St Leonards area.

In most cases, people who have gone through hardships in life become self-reliant and have high aspirations. While I was still waiting for my residency permit, I prepared myself for college and university. I combined my studies at Brighton and Sussex Universities with my new job as a Community Worker and Student Support Worker at Hastings College. I later moved on to become Student Careers Guidance Adviser and Student Support Coordinator. Two years later, I decided to take my studies even further and completed my Masters in Anthropology of Conflict, Violence and Conciliation. This involved me in a wide range of international research, peace building and media work.

Locally, I became very much involved in the voluntary and community sector in Hastings and St Leonards, which is how I became an HBC Community Cohesion Officer. With strong links in the local community, speaking five languages and some other African dialects, I am involved in promoting positive understanding between people from different backgrounds.

One role I enjoy very much is supporting local community groups, promoting the equality agenda and access to services for all. I find there is a wrong assumption that people from minority communities are homogeneous in terms of culture and needs. For example, there is no such thing as "an asylum seekers' community". That is like considering job seekers as a cultural or an ethnic group! Asylum seekers are individuals who happen to share a similar journey – that of applying for residency in the UK. As a group they include men and women of different ages with different cultural and educational backgrounds, including highly skilled professionals, who have experienced different circumstances in their own countries and arrived in the UK through different means.

The media tend to generalise by portraying inappropriate behaviour or criminal activity committed by an individual from these groups as collective behaviour or action. Inappropriate behaviour by someone who isn't easily labelled is always considered as his or her individual action and responsibility, and so it should be with asylum seekers.

Friends I met through my own journey to Hastings inspired me in many ways, for example, Athali, from Algeria: although he was not able to do well academically, he took some professional training in catering. He became a chef and ran a number of successful businesses in Hastings. He is now a popular chocolatier, running a nationwide company – but his base remains firmly in St Leonards. Athali is an entrepreneur and provides great opportunities for employment in the local area. He is a man with so many local social connections and with a great interest in promoting a positive image of migrants and the area we live in.

Another friend, Diallo, took professional training in construction and developed an interest in property management; he became a property developer and currently owns a number of properties in St Leonards and a company which also offers great job opportunities. Most of the people I have known within the newly established communities have worked hard to sustain their living, and they continue to be active members of the local community and law-abiding citizens.

New residents in St Leonards do not come only through asylum-seeking. At least 300 citizens of the new EU countries have relocated to St Leonards, enriching yet again the local cultural diversity, the interchange of ideas, and a better understanding of other peoples. It is now estimated that the proportion of people from minority communities has moved from three percent of the local population in 2001 to ten percent in 2011. In St Leonards alone, 32 languages are spoken in addition to English, with Polish, Kurdish, Arabic, Pashto, Farsi, Bengali, Mandarin, Czech, Russian, Arabic and Turkish at the top of the list.

Carnival, St Leonards Style

Photos by Tony Frost

Secret Corners of St Leonards No 6

A short cut down to the beach... but from where?

Pieces to Fit

A live performance and screendance installation curated and performed by Marina Tsartsara with Soline Pillet, Silvia Battista, Sophia Campeu-Ferman and Art in Motion. The former lifeguard station, lower promenade opposite Warrior Square Gardens, St. Leonards-on Sea. 2011-09-17.

Review by Joe Fearn

While honest men sleep on, I sneaked down the stone steps opposite Warrior Square Gardens and snook into the former lifeguard station near bottle alley in St Leonards-on-Sea.

Word was out that the spooky underground space was the venue for live performance events by artists participating in **Interface**, a cross-border collaboration initiated in response to the 20th anniversary of the formal twinning links between Hastings and Oudenaarde[1]. The town clock says 7.45pm. Seagulls on a high wire form the first bars of a sea shanty, as light drops into a bulb over the Lifeguard Station door. I descend the clammy steps, while behind me, out at sea, a cargo ship slips by like a magic-lantern image.

The venue has a clammy atmosphere. It's not unlike breathing in the damp air when walking along the roadways found down a coalmine. The artists and visitors too are crossing boundaries both external and self-imposed; through working in a cross-cultural context, many of 'the interventions' are informed by the viewpoint of the outsider, suggesting new responses to both built environment and culture. In Hastings and in St Leonards, the unconventional non-gallery art locations include public spaces, redundant outdoor sites and buildings. I was about to experience an art 'intervention' in the underpass linking the town to the promenade. The art interventions explore a range of issues such as memory, temporality, identity, history, humour, myth and popular culture. [2]

Christine Gist, artist and curator, greeted me and other curious souls who were just passing by when the light came on and drew

---

[1] Literally 'Old Earth'

[2] **Interface** evolved from 'Place' which was curated for Coastal Currents 2010 and 'From A to B', artists' interventions and performance in Dover Town centre 2010.

them in. The first artwork to come into view is by Sophia Campeu-Ferman and Art-in-Motion (Claire Whistler) called <u>Body Systems: Heart</u>, a part of a series of three, about the intimate relationship between one's body and illness. Their art deals with the commitment of the mind and body to centre and embody the process of this relationship. The form of this commitment is realised through dance, film, photographs, sound, sculpture and painting. Whistler moves within the installation, interacting with the visuals and sound. Cameu-Ferman brings that interaction together through a creation of spontaneous ink drawings. It was rum stuff.

Moving along, I found the disused male and female toilet cubicles are now venues for a work called 'carcass' which proved very evocative, and involves a textile artwork hanging upside down like a dead, skinned animal. As I moved to view the performance on the stone 'stage' at the end of the 'roadway', a clap of thunder and shaft of lightning heralded an incredible downpour that resulted in several leaks in our underground vault, something which itself became part of the whole experience. I was enjoying the Gothic nature of it all; the ink drawings by Cameu-Ferman reminded me somewhat of the pre-<u>Alien</u> film paintings of H.R. Giger.

Battista's performance <u>All Citizens of the Same Land: The Maze</u> was in a separate room just off the stairs, and is based on the metaphorical idea of the maze. A maze represents a complex multi-directional branching puzzle, a trick path with fake exits and egress, illusory repetitions and mirrors that represent the line between sanity and madness. Two giants of the film industry David Lynch and Stanley Kubrick inspire the piece, especially their explorative work on the subconscious, according to the available handout.

I went back to look into the other cubicle. A dark figure skulked inside. Not an art installation this time, but Jeremy Birch, leader of Hastings Council, who was invited to view the show.

Just beyond the toilet cubicles is a stone stage not high enough for the average person to stand up with sufficient headroom. This was the space chosen by Marina Tsartsara and Soline Pillet for a site-specific work called <u>par-A phrase</u> (sic) that explores the experience of a relationship through fragmentation. The work consists of a screendance and a live installation. For me this was the star of the show. Pillet was dynamic in her presentation of performance as visual art, with the ephemeral of the live body as a necessary layer to the work. Pillet's white dress and flowing blonde hair glided across the ceiling, at times seemingly suspended in space, with just the toes of one foot carrying the weight of her whole body. Her performance reminded me of the film The Grudge as she seemed to be struggling to stay on the ceiling and not be drawn downwards, rather than the reality of being on the ground and stretching upwards. Mind you, if her grounded leg had successfully joined the rest of her on the ceiling, I would have been out of there like a bat out of hell! I've seen too many late night vampire movies to stay and applaud.

The handout I was given says of par-A-phrase:

It focuses on the transformation of text into choreographic material, of the choreographic qualities into a filmic strategy, and of the filmic qualities into another piece of choreography that explores what is excluded from the frame, in order to produce this interdisciplinary work.

I've no idea what that means, but I really enjoyed all the work on show.

Pieces to Fit: Marina Tsarsara

Pieces to Fit: Sasha Bion

Pieces to fit: Soline Pilet & Marina Tsarsara

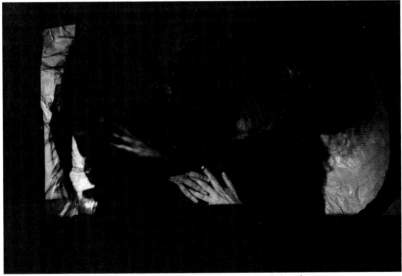

Pieces to fit: Art in Motion Claire Whistler

Norbert's Ears

Just why Norbert's left ear
Is an elongate form
Is a thing only known to his mother
But the strange fact remains
That his left and right ears
Are quite differently shaped to each other.

RR

For the right one is round
And so wondrously huge
That it flaps when the wind's blowing free.
But his left ear is long
And it's narrow and strong,
So it's useful for stirring his tea.

Tony Frost

Long-Haired William

"You are old, long-haired William," the young man said,
"And you walk like an arthritic crab.
Yet you plonk the piano with masterly ease.
How on earth are you quite such a dab?"

"It is true in the evenings," the old man replied
"I love to play jazz on the keys
But it's not as you thought, my hair is quite short
For it used to hang down to my knees."

You are old, jazzy William," the young man said
"And your coat is just holes joined by thread
Yet you quote Ezra Pound and make Eliot sound
Like a fanfare of words in my head."

"It is true I'm romantic," the old man replied
"And fine words move my soul quite a bit
But my language gets risky when laced with cheap whisky
Which changes me into a twit."

"You are old, boozy William," the young man said
"And wonderfully funny when drunk
Yet you don't have much money, your outlook's not sunny.
Don't you feel like a dreamboat that's sunk?"

"It is true I'm not wealthy," the old man replied
"And the girls let me look but not smooch
But I've had lots of fun in and out of the sun
And no woman's a match for good hooch."

Tony Frost

The Singer

To Michael, singer/songwriter at The Rooms.

The lights are low and the notes that slide
Slowly into my consciousness
Are fragments of lost memories
Drifting from somewhere in the night
To haunt me once again.

The singer's eyes are closed, his dreams
A thousand miles away from here.
Only his passion beats against
The bare walls of the bar as he strums
The mellow old guitar.

Do I know that song, or is it like
Another that I heard before,
Maybe a hundred years ago?
His words are echoes of old loves,
Snatched moments between the tears.

I want to steal his sounds and hold
Them close against my breast but they
Elude my grasp, float into night
And the pangs of memory remain
As the eastern sky grows light.

Tony Frost

Secret Corners of St Leonards No 7

Here be dragons…

…but where?

Bombed Buildings – from age seven

by Steph Stonham

"And just what do you think you're doing, young lady?"

At the sound of his voice, I start and cling onto the rough branches. My throat goes dry.

"Well, I'll have your name and address, if you please."

"My name is... is... Lousiana Bradshaw."

"Oh, it is, is it?" His voice rumbles like thunder. I'm scared to bits. "How old are you?"

"I'm seven, Sir."

"And where do you live?"

"Ninety-four London Road, Sir."

"Well you know you shouldn't be in here, don't you?"

I'm trapped. Whether I say 'yes' or 'no', I'll be in trouble.

"You'd better go home, right now"

I tumble down through hard, green apples and crunchy leaves. When I reach the ground, I take a quick glance at him – a giant in police uniform. I'm going!

Stumbling over piles of bricks and broken walls, at last I reach Church Road. Thank goodness he's too big to get through our hole in the garden wall. I run home as fast as I can. I won't tell Mum or I'll be in even more trouble. Panting, I open the door of nineteen Western Road, dash up the stairs and into my room.

There's a heavy hammering on the front door.

"Don't let it be him. Oh Lord, don't let it be him!"

I push my door open a little. It *is* him – I know his voice.

Suppose I have to go to prison. Shall I run away? How will I escape with him standing there? I can hear Mum talking and his deep voice chiming in.

The front door closes. Has he really gone? I peep out of my window. There he is, walking away down the road.

I wait a long time, then sneak downstairs. My brother and sister are waiting for me. They look cross.

"You were daft, Stephanie. Surely you knew that he'd follow you home? And now we've only got the apples we had in our pockets. And 'Granny's Garden' is the only bombed building with an apple tree."

"Yes, and now he'll be watching it. There's loads of them left lying on the ground – just wasting away."

I make a feeble effort to defend myself. "It wasn't my fault. You ran away and left me in the tree. Why is it always me who has to climb it?"

"'Cos you're the only one small enough."

"Well, it's not fair. It's just not fair. Why am I the only one to get into trouble?"

Mum calls from the kitchen and Susan goes to see what she wants.

She comes back frowning. "Mum says we've got to put all our apples on the kitchen table. Now we won't have *any*."

We're still fed up as we eat our dinner until Mum comes in with pudding. It's a huge, steaming apple pie.

"We can't waste food with all this rationing," she says, slicing the pie.

Hot custard crowns the scrumptious apple and pastry. We're soon ready for second helpings.

"Now listen," Mum says sternly. "There's to be no more playing in the bombed buildings. They are dangerous places. Do you all understand?"

"Yes, Mum," we chorus.

We don't play in 'Granny's Garden' for more than two weeks. And that's a very long time. The apples on the tree have turned to sweet red by then, just right for us to eat them.

I've made up my mind. I won't have any silly name that Susan chooses. I'll make up my next pretending name for myself. *Louisiana Bradshaw* indeed! No wonder he didn't believe me. And I'll say I live at the House of Commons. The police won't say anything to *that*.

Bombed Buildings – from age seventy

by Steph Stonham

Naked houses, ruined, humbled
secrets all laid bare
gaping roofs, bricks to rubble –
we children had no care.

Carpets stained with dirt and rain
we would never know the pain.
Victors over rival gangs,
where the tattered paper hangs
squatters we, all unaware
how they thronged the broken stair.

Are their ghosts still with me now?
Life has made me blind.
Memory extinguishes the years
Those early times do bind.

We play together without tears
              within my secret mind.

Water Rises

Water rises, back arched, a panther
poised and ready to strike – wind
pushing, whipping, spurring it on
as the swell surges, pounces
on its prey. Steely grey
turns into foam and spray
as mountains shatter, a
thousand droplets tossed
clumsily up to the air, nowhere
else to go but down, down upon
that jagged face, and fall amidst
the craggy places; a peppering
of watery shards, glinting
in the winter air. No sooner
seen, they disappear, roll
down into the surf beneath, and
giants carry them to shore
to burrow there amongst the sand.

Zelda Chappel

Gathered

Gathered they are vultures
under gulls' guise forming
in overhead patterns
of sweeping lines, pacing
building their momentum
adding wing after wing
in pairs.

Waiting, their eagerness
filters down through blue air
resting heavy on heads
of weekend seasiders
threatened by unfamiliar
rules of beach-placed etiquette
and theft

happening instant – a clash
of wings on flesh and beaks
sharp with promise, piercing
skin, jabbing boldly in one
accurately violent snatch
decisive, focused
executed.

Zelda Chappel

Secret Corners of St Leonards No 8

There are some fascinating corners of St Leonards where local arts and crafts people and traders exhibit their work. Do you know where to find the lady (left) who runs this treasure-store?

Pyramid Square

An alternative future
by Jo Moon

Image © 2012 Heather Hawthorn

I guess I had brushed with the past often, down the old Kings Road and London Road. It was funny to see how they used to be full of pubs and meat shops and places where you could buy liquor poison and that kind of thing. I had seen in the museum how people used to walk down the streets with smoke coming out of their mouths – nicotine, and how people ambled about begging for money. They didn't have the fund then, and few healers, so it wasn't easy for them. I felt sorry for those times and those who had nothing more to do than search for these intoxicating substances. My heart went out to the past and that was why we were having the 'healing the past' gathering in Pyramid Square. The past had to be dealt with entirely now so as to clear energies away. I often viewed it through my third eye: the scenes outside pubs and cafés where ideas were exchanged between artists, and better ways sought – but they often had a glass or cup of poison in their hands, blurring the vision.

The square had been inundated with swarms of flying ants and beetles for weeks now, which seemed to symbolize negative energies rising up again. I had them caught up in my hair and nails. The city health council met and declared that we needed to rid the air of negative history pollution. I was looking forward to the event, and to seeing Jack again. He was nearing his 140th year and could almost remember those long lost times of ancient St Leonards! At least he had heard the stories from his grandfather and often talked of times when he was offered beer and cigarettes as a boy of only nine and ten. I shuddered to think of such a thing.

The golden pyramid was gleaming in the square against a rising sun. People were on their way to the prayer gathering and early morning chant. I was going to miss it today, in favour of a walk along the lanes which led directly to the East Hill. At sunrise I would be able to hear the chanting as I ambled my way there. I watched as people in their white, orange and lilac gowns emerged from their solar-powered huts and gave their peace greetings against the rising golden-red and orange sun. I felt a knowingness in my heart that everything would be well today and we would extract the fumes of the past forever.

The boy, Lincoln, appeared. 'Hey Solarias where are you off to?' He came running up behind me and sounded urgent.

'Just meandering up to the hill Linc. What are you up to?'

'My dad's sick – can you help him? He can hardly get out of bed and his alarm's gone off. His health has gone down a lot. Don't know what healers are around now. Can you come Solarias?'

I shuddered to think of Ben in his small hut, unable to move, it was such a rare thing these days. 'I'll come Lincoln, but please go to the prayer gathering now and tell them to pray for your father.'

He rushed off inside the pyramid and I made my way to their home. Billowing smoke was making waves out of the roof – at least they had the warmth of their woodburner inside, even if it was a bit ancient.

I walked in.

'Ben?'

A crumpled up man was lying under thick hemp blankets – too thick for springtime. He was wheezing and congested in his lungs. 'What's happened Ben? Did you give up on something?'

'Come here Solarias, and bring water please. I'm dying. Can't get back my strength. Just help me pass over peacefully. I don't want to carry on any more. Get me that jug of crystal water please...'

I rushed over with a glass of water and the clear quartz crystal. 'Are you sure you want to go Ben?'

'My time's at an end Solarias. Those days from the past are creeping up on me. I'm one of the elders that has to go. You know, ever since Rose left me I can't live happily any more.'

'But what about the love-finders, Ben? You could find yourself a new wife or companion. Do you not want that?' I placed my hands on his heart chakra and sent out pink rays of love.

'I don't want that. I've had enough Solarias. I miss her so much. I just want to join her again. There'll never be another one like her. Just send me away will you? Do the ritual with Lincoln – he'll understand.'

'Is he ready Ben? Will he cope?'

'He's a strong boy – take care of him for me will you?'

I felt concerned. I couldn't look after Lincoln full time. 'I'll get a group together, Ben, and we'll share the care of Linc. I can't do it all.'

'He's 14. He'll be all right.'

The little wooden door flew open and Lincoln rushed in, flushed and in a sweat. 'He's going, isn't he?' he managed to mumble in my direction. I nodded back. Lincoln approached his father and clasped his hands while soft tears rolled down his cheeks. 'I love you father – will you not reconsider?'

'I'm going Linc, my boy, I love you but I can't live here without my Rose. I'll talk to you from the other side. I'll help ya. It'll be all right. Solarias and others will look after you.'

Lincoln cried more, and I held both of them strongly. I lit six candles and surrounded the rose quartz crystals with their gleaming light. The essential oils of rosemary and sage lay in a pot which I burnt for letting go. He had it all arranged long ago. Lincoln pulled the gold cover from under the bed and placed it over his father, who was now smiling. I took the holy water from the urn and placed a dab onto his third eye for protection and inner-seeing.

'Is there anyone you wish to forgive, Ben?'

He promptly handed me a long, hand written list he held under the bed covers. 'I've been thinking about it a long time Solarias. I want to release all my enemies now. No, they're not enemies of course, just the ones I struggled with – the bank manager who took all my money back in the bank days!' Lincoln chuckled. 'They won't find any use for that now, will they?'

I took my golden pendulum from under my skirt and waved it over the list. 'May all these people and beings of love be forgiven for any acts, thoughts or defaults that have negatively affected Ben over the years and may Ben and they be released from any guilt or negativity.'

Ben gave a terrific sigh and his wheezing diminished immediately. 'What would you like to say Ben?'

'I love all my family, I love you all. I love this town, St Leonards that has given me a home for so many years. I am grateful for the past, present and future. I wish for this town to thrive and grow with more strength than ever before, to make this an even brighter future for everyone. May love and healing thrive in all ways, and may I join with my beloved Rose once more and do my light work from above.'

He breathed deeply, and Lincoln was almost bruising his father's hands from squeezing so tightly. I nodded at Lincoln.

'What would you like to say Linc?'

'I love you so much, father. I'm sorry you're leaving me. I will do what I can to carry on your work, to be a warrior and healer-musician for the people. I will talk to you when you're gone and ask for your advice often. Thank you for all you have ever done for me and please forgive me for any acts I have done against you.'

'My son. You are perfect and never could I have wished for a better son than you. Follow your own path now and see to it that you join with your heart's desire when you are ready. Love and be loved and you are always safe. Farewell to you Lincoln. I am going to a lighter place now but you will be well cared for here I know it.'

The time was nearing completion now. I had not expected it to be so quick.

'I love you Ben. Please talk to us in the meditation and channelling sessions if you wish, and thank you for your time here in St Leonards, giving us all hope and joy from your singing and music. Now may your passing over be calm and peaceful and one of many blessings.' I sprinkled rose petals over his head and holy water over his temples. 'Blessings to you forever our beloved one!'

He closed his eyes softly and went away. I pressed my right hand to Lincoln's and we watched as Ben's soul was lifted upwards to the other dimension. We cried and hugged each other.

That was my unexpected morning, and now I had a new son. We had a meeting later on in the day and discussed how a group of us would care for Lincoln. I was to move to a shanty hut next to Lincoln's. Lincoln would live alone, but with many of us around him to help. I looked forward to listening to his minstrel-sound of healing music and to his stories, and watching him dance. It would be a pleasure to watch him grow up. I had no children of my own to care for. My role was that of a healer and care-giver to whoever needed my help at any time. I never knew what would happen from one day to the next. Just walked my path wherever it led, and prayed that the right outcome would happen every day.

The body was buried at sunset along with others on the West Hill. It seemed fitting to bury Ben on the day of the 'healing the past' ritual. I had not expected him to go so suddenly but it was his wish and he and Lincoln were eventually happy.

I took the lane up to the East Hill early afternoon, breathing in the smells of the sea, incense burning from the temples and raw chocolate from the cafe on the seafront. I'd already had my raw chocolate fix for the day in the form of raw chocolate chai followed by raw chocolate cheesecake! Amazing. Life felt so much easier now all the banks had closed down. We just did our work whatever it was, got paid in rupees and then bought whatever we needed. There was always the hardship fund for anyone not able to earn a lot, but it was hardly ever used. Everyone had something to offer, and everyone was paid. I got 100 rupees for sending Ben over. Lincoln got paid wherever he played his music. The law of exchange was followed in earnest here. St Leonards was a fair place to live and no-one went without. Those days were long gone.

It was hard to think back to the time of the Earthquake but that's when it all finally changed. It was like a crashing down of some old system that didn't work any more and once that crack surfaced all over town, bringing down buildings and, basically, the past, it all had to be re-built. They brought in a new band of town planners, healers, psychics and healing-minstrels and together we brought a totally new ethos and energy to the town. We have always given many thanks to

God for such a catalyst to spark a new beginning, but many were not thanking anyone at the time. It appeared to be an absolute catastrophe. But then, catalysts and catastrophes are very similar and yet create diverse reactions.

I liked meandering down the East Hill lanes and pondering on things, it was my favourite activity. I was so happy that the nature lanes from St Leonards to the East Hill had been created. I loved the flowers, trees, springs, fairies and elementals. It was a magical walk and delightful to connect the two neighbouring towns in this way.

I would return to town just in time for the 'healing the past' gathering and just in time to buy some vegetable waffles and fruit salad from Veggies-a-go-go cafe-shop. And just in time to sit by the wise old oak tree at the corner of Kings Road and watch Lincoln play his flute and sing some tunes of positivity for the future. I would help Lincoln connect to his father often and we would pray together every evening. I was looking forward to being a carer for Lincoln and I was sure he would teach me a lot too. He was one of the latest Rainbow children and they have a lot to give to the world.

Thank you for reading this. Its time for our 'Healing the Past' meeting now. I had a lovely walk and now we are going to release all negativity from the past of St Leonards so the ants and beetles will leave us in peace and the flowers will grow for ever, more beautiful by the minute. The angels are with us. They tell us so every day through the joy that fills our hearts and the healing that inspires new beginnings and the love that is bountiful in every way – for that is the nature of LOVE.

You can find more of Jo's sci-fi at
www.jomoonvisions.com

90

Secret Corners of St Leonards No 9

Do you know who invented unvandalism (the art of making pictures by selectively cleaning up grubby walls and pavements) or where you can find these examples of their work in St Leonards?

You are Meant to be Five

by Rosamond Palmer

I am in a cot. At home I sleep in a bed but here in Buchanan Hospital, I am in a cot. All the cots are white; the legs have wheels on them and the side-bars go up and down. There are a lot of children here. It's a big room; this is what it looks like:

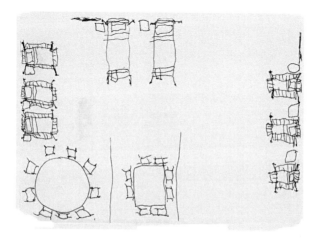

All the other children are up and playing. The girl who sleeps next to me stands at the bottom of my cot; she hangs onto a curtain that comes from high up. She looks cross.

"How old are you?" she asks.

"Four," I tell her.

"I'm five."

I don't say anything.

"You are meant to be five when you go to hospital," she says, like I've done something wrong. I don't think she is right but she is older than me.

"Do you want your curtains pulled?" she asks.

I don't know what she means, so I say, "No."

She pulls the material around my cot and I can't see out.

Her head comes through where the curtains join. "There you are, I've closed your curtains for you."

She goes away. I don't like her.

My feet feel sticky. I lift my toes up so I can feel the top sheet on the bottom of my feet; air goes between my toes.

A nurse with yellow hair opens up my curtains and puts a big bowl of white ice-cream and a spoon on my table. It's good because my throat is sore and when I swallow the cold ice-cream, I don't feel the hurt.

I like the nurses. They are 'smiley' and pretty, they wear dresses, white aprons and stiff white hats, they look very clean. They walk about quickly and quietly and speak to us and one another nicely.

Beside my cot are two tables, one the nurses put in front of me so I can have my dinner, it feels like smooth wood; the other one, the nurses put a golden fizzy drink on, it tastes funny.

I like the orange juice Mummy gets from the clinic. It comes in a clear glass bottle, with square sides, the same as the cod liver oil. The orange is very thick, but they don't have that here. At home we are given cod liver oil – it's stinky and makes me feel sick, and we have malt – that tastes better. They don't give us cod liver oil or malt in this hospital; we get ice-cream and a golden fizzy drink.

We have breakfast, dinner and tea in bed. Every day we get the same dinner. It's minced up meat, cabbage and mashed potato and makes the room smell wet.

After dinner we have a little rest, then a bell goes and all the mummies come in. I hope Mummy remembers to bring Bunny, I don't really want Bunny but I want her to remember I want him. I've got Teddy already.

There is a little blackboard in the playroom and I asked Mummy to buy me some chalks. I want to take them out of their box and put them back in. There is a jigsaw here that I really like. I play with it every day.

All the children are in bed. Two nurses wheel a big trolley to the cots; it squeaks and rattles. On top of the trolley are enormous white jugs. They take the trolley to a cot and then close the curtains. Then they open the curtains and go to the next cot. There is a smell of rubber and poo. I can see that I'm going to be next. They rattle in the trolley, one nurse takes down the side of my cot and the other nurse closes the curtains. The nurses stand either side of my cot. The nurse next to the trolley picks up a long brown tube and looks at it. They turn me on my side. I can hear water pouring, it's going inside me.

"Is your tummy full?" asks the nurse who is behind me.

"No," I say and shake my head, so she does more pouring.

"Is it full now?" she asks.

"No," I tell her.

The nurse who is looking at me says, "That'll do."

On the floor is a white, enamel potty, it's the same one as we have at home. There is a blue band around the top. When I sit on it, the edge presses into my bottom and the back of the tops of my legs, it hurts. On the trolley are lots of potties with bent in sides. We don't have any like that at home.

I sit on the white one. The nurse who did the pouring is very tall. She is holding a roll of crackly toilet paper. Mummy buys Bronco but this toilet paper doesn't smell like Bronco, it smells a bit like the water the lady in a green coat washes the floor with.

"I want to do a poo," I tell the tall nurse.

"That's what it's for," she says.

Everyone else is in bed and I'm allowed up. I've got on my nightie, dressing gown and slippers. At the other end of the room, near where the mummies come in, there is a little girl I like. I stand at the bottom of her cot and talk to her. I want to do a poo and it comes out. I feel it drop to the floor between my feet. No one can see it; it's hidden underneath my dressing gown. I don't say anything, I walk away.

There isn't anyone to play with. All the other children are in their cots with the sides up. I can't get near them. I find the nurse with yellow hair.

"You want to go back to bed now?"

I nod and she puts me back.

I'm sitting up in my cot, watching the nurses come in and out of the kitchen.

The tall one says, "Have you seen what's on the floor over there?"

I think she has found my poo. I hope they think someone else did it.

Now three nurses are talking about the poo on the floor. One says "It must have been Jenny, she's the only one who has been up."

94

"It wasn't. It wasn't me," I scream from my cot.

The tall nurse comes and wipes my bottom but I don't think she finds any poo.

Next to the kitchen there are two big boys in beds. I think they are brothers, they look the same. They don't play with us, they read comics and books.

In the morning, the nurses come round and put glass sticks in our mouths and undo the buttons on our pyjama tops. The big boys sit still, their chests are bare. Then the nurses come round and take the glass sticks out of our mouths and look at them. They do writing on brown wooden things that they keep at the bottom of our cots. Then doctors come and walk round and leave.

The nurses undo our buttons in case the doctors want to listen to our chests. My chest is bad. Mummy says I've got bronchitis and I can't go home. When children have their tonsils out, they stay here for a week. I've had my tonsils out but I have to stay longer.

When the bell rings, the door opens and the mummies come in. My Mummy kisses me. I hope the nurses haven't told Mummy about the poo.

"Have you brought my chalks?"

"Yes." She takes a small white paper bag out of her handbag and gives it to me. I look inside it and the chalks are just in the bag.

"Are they all right?" she asks.

"Yes," I lie. "I thought they'd be in a box."

"So did I," says Mummy. "But that's how he gave them to me."

I know the bag will fall apart.

"What's that?" I say, seeing another white paper bag.

"It's sweets."

"Can I have them?"

"No, I have to give them to the nurses and then they share them out. I had better hand them in."

She takes them to the kitchen and comes back.

"Here's Bunny."

I take him.

A nurse gives me a spoonful of medicine. It tastes of sweet raspberries. I swallow it, Mummy watches me. The nurse gives me a big toffee in a wrapper that is twisted at both ends. Mummy watches me unwrap the toffee and put it in my mouth. It's sweet and chewy, but doesn't taste as good as the medicine. I tell Mummy that the medicine here is nice, I don't think she is listening to me but she says "Mmm," I think she is upset about the chalks. I don't want her to be upset.

I'm in the bath; the nurse with short red hair has washed me. I slosh the water around with my hands. The room smells of soap.

The nurse sits down. "You can have a play now."

There are lots of toys at the end of the bath. I want her to put them all in. She thinks I only want one or two. I wonder if the other children only have one or two. I point at the toys and nod.

"You want all of them in?" She sounds surprised.

I keep nodding and one at a time, she plops them in. They make little splashes. I can't see the water and I don't know how to play with them. I like the game of her plopping them in better.

In the middle of the big room is a small room with a table, chairs and toys. I'm playing with the other children. My throat and chest don't hurt so much.

Nurses bring in a trolley of ice-cream tubs. When Mummy buys us an ice-cream from the men who sell them from big tricycles on the seafront, we have cornets. Grown-ups have tubs. Tubs come with little wooden spoons in a paper wrapper, and grown-ups eat the ice-cream straight out of the tub with the wooden spoon. I thought we'd eat the ice-cream straight out of the tubs, but here in hospital, the nurses take the ice-cream out of the tubs and put it in bowls. Then they give it to us with a metal spoon, not the wooden ones inside a wrapper.

I want to do a poo, I can't see the nurse with blond hair so I tell another nurse and she tells me to do it in the lavatory.

96

It's teatime, we have sandwiches or bread and jam, and then we have the sweets the mummies have brought in. On my plate are pieces of bread cut into triangles and between the bread are slices of banana. I suppose it is a banana sandwich. I've not seen this before. I eat bananas out of their skins; they don't go into sandwiches. I don't know if anyone else has ever seen a banana sandwich. I call to a nurse who comes over.

"These are banana sandwiches," I explain.

She looks puzzled too.

"I don't like banana sandwiches."

She takes them away, I eat the Dolly Mixture.

Every night, when it gets dark, the nurses take their books and papers to the big round table next to the window. A light with a round shade hangs from the ceiling. A nurse wraps a dark cloth round the lampshade so the light just goes on the table. I want to watch them; they all sit quietly reading and writing; all the other children are asleep. The nurses see me and nod to one another. A nurse with grey hair says "Lie down Jenny and go to sleep, or I'll give you something to make you go to sleep." I lie down.

When it's light, two nurses wheel me in my cot to the other end of the room; near where I did the poo. The little girl I like isn't there any more; I think she has gone home. I hope Mummy knows where I am.

The bell goes and the mummies come in and I watch the back of Mummy's coat walking away from me. I want to call out but I don't want the other mummies to look at me. I want Mummy, but she has gone. My cheeks are wet and my chest jumps up and down. I can hear the air sucking in and out of my mouth and nose.

Mummy is with the tall nurse, she points at my cot. They both walk towards me. Mummy is here.

"Sorry, I'm sorry. I didn't know they had moved you."

Mummy cuddles me.

I'm playing with my favourite jigsaw and then Mummy is there. It is playtime, not the time when the mummies come.

"I've come to take you home."

I want to take the jigsaw. "I can have this," I tell Mummy.

"Are you sure?" she asks.

"Yes," I lie. "The nurse said I can take it."

"I had better check," says Mummy.

I see her speaking to the tall nurse; I'm going to get into trouble.

Mummy comes back "Seems to be all right." She puts the jigsaw into a bag.

I feel bad inside because I told a lie and I'm very pleased I have the jigsaw. Mummy holds my hand and we go home.

Secret Corners of St Leonards No 10

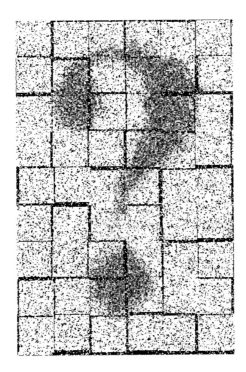

This image is in place of a photograph of the painted tiles which used to grace the wall of the children's ward at the old Buchanan hospital. The panels of tiles were handpainted by Margaret Thompson, said to be one of Doulton's best artists.

We haven't got a photo because they disappeared in mysterious circumstances some years ago and have never been found. A £3,000 reward was offered by the local NHS Trust for their return so if you know where they are...

Two Sides to Every Story

Little Bo-Peep has lost her sheep
and doesn't know where to find them.
Leave them alone
and they'll come home
wagging their tails behind them!

Or to put it another way...

It was never easy for the Customs and Excise men to find smugglers while they were at sea. There were so many little boats bobbing about out there and the smugglers' craft often had their contraband on the ends of ropes, bobbing along behind.

At the first sign of Customs activity, it was a moment's work to cut them loose and just sit there looking innocent. It was, however, sometimes easier for "Bo Peep" to catch them on the beach, after they'd hauled the barrels a-shore.

Don't go thinking smuggling and piracy were purely Old Towners' activities!

Secret Corners of St Leonards No 11

St Leonards still has a large number of unique, independent shops. They are becoming a rarity in some towns, so don't forget to enjoy ours.
Do you know which one this is?

Starfish

I am breathing
in sea, dipping
toes in salt
as awkward soles
mould to pebbles,
standing

at water's edge
foam falling
between shingle
gentle waves

bringing home
a starfish, now
shore-bound,
wrapped in
seaweed shrouds,
and covered
in shingle sand

Zelda Chappel

Morning

Sitting, listening to the waves roll in, a gentle clatter
amplified through flint and chalk and shell
as water rushes through, over and under and over again,
my idle fingers found a shell amongst the debris

battered smooth, just enough to put my thumb print in
perfectly, as if made for me, as sun battles wind
both claiming victories, minor and short-lived
and light dances like a child amongst the crests and stones.
Seagulls, braver in the morning light it seems,
scavenge amidst the seaweed and cuttlefish

bones brought in on midnight's tide
and enjoy their moment before the sun moves
slowly up from the horizon, shadows changing, shrinking away,
enticing invaders from the streets down onto the beach.

Zelda Chappel

The art of decorating walls and frontages didn't die out with the departure of local painter, decorator (and author) Robert Tressell. Do you know which road is graced by these embellished houses?

You Have to Draw the Line Somewhere

by Kay Green

In the final stages of compiling this book, some doubts sprang up over a couple of the photos. Were they actually in St Leonards, or Hastings? There's no official boundary any more. The council merged the administrative districts well over a century ago – *The Hastings Chronicle* website has a quote that suggests this prospective marriage was causing concern before it started: "We hope the inhabitants of both portions of the borough will do their best to promote a good feeling between the old and the new towns: that the close municipal union of these two may not be marred by the slightest approach to the absurd savagery of the Kilkenny cats." (From the *Hastings News* 10th October 1873).

So I was looking for a historical boundary, not anything that exists today. Here's a chart of Mr Burton's original building plot:

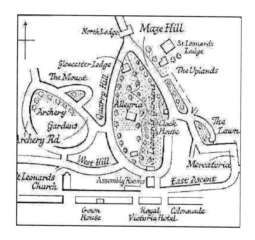

This gives us a very small area indeed, and puts Kings Road, London Road and St Leonards railway station outside the borders of St Leonards. Perhaps there is a more modern line. The post office post-code-finder happily plots TN38 as St Leonards, whereas my own address, in TN34, is Hastings. I started asking people, and receiving an extraordinary variety of responses. Everyone knows whether they are 'a Hastings person' or 'a St Leonards person' and, having firmly placed their own address in the preferred district, will then wave their arms in a general arc beyond their own property to demonstrate where *the other one* starts.

There certainly are a lot of ways of working it out. An afternoon poring over books and charts left me with the choices of Mr Burton's original building plot (see previous page) – but the new town development area Burton defined was later extended – or there are the Victorian boundary stones, or the St Leonards Church parish boundary, or there's the postal district. If I wanted to include all the people who tell me they live in St Leonards, I'd have to use a bit of all of those lines. I decided to call in the experts. First, I went and asked at the library. They had a rummage and triumphantly came up with a map with districts, including St Leonards, marked in purple felt-tip – but according to their map, there's a chunk of the town in between Hastings and St Leonards, called 'Bohemia'. As soon as I saw it, I agreed with it. I've often heard, and used, the term 'Bohemia' for the area around Bohemia Road. But where is the boundary...? Oh no!

The librarians were still rummaging. Most of the older maps we found didn't have to draw lines – it was clear that St Leonards was one little conurbation, and Hastings another, because before the 1800s, there was a lot of space in between them. Strangely though, Silverhill was a third separate conurbation, a couple of miles inland with its own name marked on the map – so the ASDA incident I described at the start of this book becomes more mysterious yet.

Of the modern maps, some put the name 'St Leonards' somewhere in the sea, in the general area of the Royal Victoria hotel but none had a line or an inland marker. Half an hour later, the library reference desk littered with maps and charts, we agreed that I should try the post office and the town hall and come back and tell the librarians when I'd found out.

The post office staff went into a huddle. Eventually, someone emerged and told me to go to the town hall or the tourist office. I pointed out that the tourist office is in the town hall but, such a day was I having, on my way there I started thinking that perhaps the area apparently within the town hall that's the tourist office probably is not, technically, the town hall...

...but the tourist office had the mayor in it when I arrived, so it must count. I learned that there was a plinth outside the Royal Victoria on the seafront that marks St Leonards. It took me a few moments to register the problem with this: From which direction? If the plinth at the Royal Vic marked the western boundary, then The Crown House wasn't included – and it ought to be, as The Crown House bears this plaque on the front...

...but if the Royal Vic marks the eastern boundary then the entire St Leonards Festival is being held in Hastings, and what of Burton's arch? It stood once, on the seafront, a hundred yards or so west of London Road, and was built to mark the eastern extent of St Leonards. At least I think it was – it's not there any more. It was purchased by the council in the 1890s with a view to demolition, as it was committing that cardinal sin of the modern age – slowing the traffic. It would appear that not many people wanted it pulled down and so Hastings Council dealt with the situation by demolishing it at night without telling anyone in advance. Ah, the joys of democracy!

But working out where the boundary is on the seafront isn't so much of a problem. Everyone has a broadly similar view of which bits of the seafront count as St Leonards. The problem starts when you try to draw a line inland. London Road is St Leonards, isn't it. King's Road most definitely is. And probably Silverhill – but Bohemia Road? And what about Warrior Square, the show-piece of the St Leonards festival?

My advisors at the town hall had agreed that there was someone in Hastings History House in the Old Town who would know how to decide, but I decided instead to turn to someone who I know has a long experience of recording the history of the town from the point of view of its residents...

Local historian Victoria Seymour says: "Where to 'draw the line' between Hastings and St Leonards has become rather vague to me. In research for my books I have caught whiffs of the snobbery that used to exist; St Leonards folk thinking that Hastings was rowdy, tripper-ridden and low class, while Hastings residents regarded the St Leonards lot as a bit above themselves. So in past times there was a social boundary but the removal of the arch in 1895 removed the certainty. I expect if today you ask six different people the question you would get as many different responses. For the purposes of your book I would disregard postcodes, the reference library, the tourist information office and just ask six people, to illustrate how vague the whole thing has become.

110

"The flexibility of such matters is illustrated by a quote from Richard Pitcairn-Knowles's new book[1]. Writing of his grandfather, Andrew, opening the Riposo Health Hydro on the Ridge in 1912, Richard says, 'The house was, from a post office point of view, in St Leonards-on-Sea, the boundary running up Grange Road. So Andrew Pitcairn-Knowles went to the trouble of having the postal boundary moved by the obliging post office so that his address could be in Hastings.'

"For me, seafront St Leonards starts at Warrior Square, with the WWII bullet-punctured knee of the Queen Victoria Statue[2]. The fact that it has never been been repaired is just so Hastings... Sorry! St Leonards."

The thing is, there are people in St Leonards who sense that it's a very important distinction but, it would appear, some of them don't know that they don't know where the boundary is until you put them on the spot by asking them. What a strange animal a sense of identity is.

Take the matter of famous residents. My own area of interest is books and authors and so I immediately think of Sheila Kaye-Smith, George MacDonald, Henry Rider Haggard, Robert Tressell... Some are more clearly identified with the locality than others. Robert Tressell (Robert Noonan) was born in Ireland, lived for more than a few years in Africa, and died in Liverpool – but his famous work, *The Ragged Trousered Philanthropists* was most definitely born in Hastings (argh – I mean St Leonards) and not just because he wrote it here (reputedly during his time living at 241 London Road). The reason I say this is that Hastings and St Leonards *caused* the book to happen, especially St Leonards. Burton's new town project was designed to attract a new community of affluent, genteel people. The houses were tall, elegant, spacious, graced with attractive public gardens... it was vital that the new residents be affluent because the area didn't have enough of an industrial base to provide business, work and wages to new people of the type that needed an income.

---

[1] 'Celebrating the Centenary of The Founding of RIPOSO HEALTH HYDRO in Hastings 1912-2012' by Richard Pitcairn-Knowles
[2] See photo on page 24

By the time Robert Noonan turned up in St Leonards though, the new town had grown beyond Burton's original plans and the new community included plenty of people who needed jobs and/or business opportunities. The logical result was that there weren't enough jobs to go around, and working conditions were hard. For a man like Noonan, used to a warmer climate and already aware of a growing problem with his lungs, it was shocking. Getting up before 6am to walk miles in the rain to find building, decorating or signwriting work that didn't pay well enough for a man to eat or live well gave him a very clear idea indeed of what bad working conditions were like. He was desperate to show how self-defeating it was for the businessmen to cut and scrimp to beat each other to scarce contracts, and for the workers in turn to accept ever-lower wages and ever-longer hours in order to get the work before their fellows, and so *The Ragged Trousered Philanthropists* was born.

The fortunes of St Leonards and Hastings have risen and fallen as different eras pass. Sometimes one seems more affluent, sometimes the other. Recently, St Leonards has taken on an interesting, Bohemian feel, with a wonderful variety of artistic enterprises springing up – and Hastings has just got itself an art gallery – but many people are 'feeling the pinch', and thinking the lessons of *The Ragged Trousered Philanthropists* haven't been learned yet. The book remains popular.

When the players from the London Irish Theatre came to St Leonards to present a dramatic reading of their (Irish) hero's work at the Crown House, I took them on a tour of the places where you can no longer see examples of Robert Tressell's signwriting. I can remember when the house at the end of Perth Road looked like this:

...and I can remember it catching my eye and making me think modern advertisements just haven't got that kind of style. I can't remember when it was painted over. It was about a decade later, when it was long gone, that I discovered it was by one of Hastings and St Leonards' most famous authors. The kind of things I was asking the London Irish players to look at were more like this:

...we weren't at all sure that any of the walls we were looking at had ever felt the brush of the great man but never had I seen a huddle of rapt cultural tourists gaze so lovingly at so many examples of down-at-heel brick walls.

And the moral of this story is: it's not the facts that count to the human heart, it's the sense of history. Like King Arthur, Father Christmas and the perfect partner, St Leonards definitely exists and if you are a St Leonards person at heart, your house, and your favourite pubs, cafés, shops and parks are all definitely in it.

Secret Corners of St Leonards No 13

If you've lived in Hastings and St Leonards for long,
you've probably read this intriguing piece of pavement...
but is it in St Leonards or Hastings?

~~ The End ~~

~or possibly the start~